D1538893

ALGEBRAIC GEOMETRY

Introduction to Schemes

MATHEMATICS LECTURE NOTE SERIES

E. Artin and J. Tate *Harvard University*	CLASS FIELD THEORY
Michael Atiyah *Oxford University*	K-THEORY
Hyman Bass *Columbia University*	ALGEBRAIC K-THEORY
Raoul Bott *Harvard University*	LECTURES ON K(X)
Paul J. Cohen *Stanford University*	SET THEORY AND THE CONTINUUM HYPOTHESIS
Walter Feit *Yale University*	CHARACTERS OF FINITE GROUPS
Marvin J. Greenberg *Northeastern University*	LECTURES ON ALGEBRAIC TOPOLOGY
Robin Hartshorne *Harvard University*	FOUNDATIONS OF PROJECTIVE GEOMETRY
Serge Lang *Columbia University*	ALGEBRAIC FUNCTIONS
Serge Lang *Columbia University*	RAPPORT SUR LA COHOMOLOGIE DES GROUPES
I. G. Macdonald *Oxford University*	ALGEBRAIC GEOMETRY: INTRODUCTION TO SCHEMES
George Mackey *Harvard University*	INDUCED REPRESENTATIONS OF GROUPS AND QUANTUM MECHANICS
Richard Palais *Brandeis University*	FOUNDATIONS OF GLOBAL NON-LINEAR ANALYSIS
Jean-Pierre Serre *Collège de France*	ABELIAN l-ADIC REPRESENTATIONS AND ELLIPTIC CURVES
Jean-Pierre Serre *Collège de France*	ALGEBRES DE LIE SEMI-SIMPLES COMPLEXES
Jean-Pierre Serre *Collège de France*	LIE ALGEBRAS AND LIE GROUPS

ALGEBRAIC GEOMETRY

Introduction to Schemes

I. G. MACDONALD

Oxford University

W. A. BENJAMIN, INC.

New York 1968 Amsterdam

ALGEBRAIC GEOMETRY: Introduction to Schemes

QA 564
.M3
1968

Copyright © 1968 by W. A. Benjamin, Inc.
All rights reserved

Library of Congress Catalog Card Number 68-28140
Manufactured in the United States of America

*The manuscript was put into production on March 29, 1968;
this volume was published on June 7, 1968*

INDIANA
UNIVERSITY
LIBRARY

NORTHWEST

W. A. BENJAMIN, INC.
New York, New York 10016

FOREWORD

These notes are based on lectures given at the University of Sussex in 1964-65. Their aim was to provide an introduction to the language of schemes, for an audience consisting largely of classical geometers, but in fact they cover little more than the basic local theory. In principle, nothing is assumed of the reader beyond elementary notions of algebra and topology.

I am indebted to Dr. J. A. Tyrrell of King's College, London, for assistance in preparing these notes for publication.

CONTENTS

Chapter 1

INTRODUCTION

The subject-matter of algebraic geometry, from the time of Descartes onwards, has been the study of the solutions of systems of polynomial equations in several variables:

$$f_\alpha(x_1, \ldots, x_n) = 0. \qquad (1)$$

Originally the f_α were taken to have real coefficients, and one looked for real solutions. However, fairly soon it was realised that it made better sense to include complex solutions, since there was then a better chance of their existence (e.g., $x^2 + y^2 + 1 = 0$ has no real solutions, but plenty of complex ones).

Equally, one of the main preoccupations of number theory has been Diophantine problems, i.e., the solutions (if any) of a system of equations (1) in rational integers, the f_α now being supposed to have integer coefficients: for example, 'Fermat's last theorem', the equation $x^n + y^n = z^n$. As this example indicates, the problem thus set was often too hard, so it was natural to modify it by asking either for rational solutions or for solutions mod. p (p a prime number), i.e., to regard the equations (1) as having their coefficients in the rational field $\underline{Q}$ or the finite field $\underline{F}_p$ and to ask for solutions in that field. More generally, we may reduce the equations (1) mod. p^n, thereby replacing the coefficient domain by the Artin local ring $\underline{Z}/(p^n)$, and we may then pass to the ring of p-adic integers $\underline{Z}_p = \varprojlim \underline{Z}/(p^n)$, or its field of fractions $\underline{Q}_p$.

Thus it is natural to consider systems of equations (1) with coefficient domains other than the fields of real or complex numbers, and these coefficient domains may not always be fields. However, if we stick to a coefficient field, we had better let it be quite arbitrary if we want a theory which is of sufficient generality for its applications. In particular, our field should be allowed to have positive characteristic (e.g., the finite fields). So we are led to study the solutions of (1), where the f_α are now polynomials over an arbitrary field k. As already observed, it is not enough to consider only the solutions in k, because there may not be any, or at any rate not enough: we should therefore take an algebraically closed field $K \supseteq k$, and consider the solutions of (1) in K. This is roughly the point of view of Weil (Foundations of Algebraic Geometry). If we agree to ignore questions of rationality, we can jettison k and use only K. But this is inadequate for many purposes, e.g., Weil's conjectures on the number of points of an algebraic variety over a finite field.

AFFINE ALGEBRAIC GEOMETRY

Let k be a field, K an algebraically closed field containing k, and let S be a subset of the polynomial ring $k[t_1, \ldots, t_n]$ (which we shall abbreviate to $k[t]$). The variety V(X) defined by S is the set of all $x = (x_1, \ldots, x_n) \in K^n$ such that $f(x) = 0$ for all $f \in S$. If $\underline{a}$ is the ideal generated by S in $k[t]$, then clearly $V(S) = V(\underline{a})$. Now let $\underline{a}^*$ be the ideal consisting of all $f \in k[t]$ which vanish at every point of V. Clearly $\underline{a}^* \supseteq \underline{a}$, and the inclusion may be strict (for example, $\underline{a} = (t_1^2)$, $\underline{a}^* = (t_1)$). The relationship between $\underline{a}$ and $\underline{a}^*$ is given by a theorem of Hilbert (the Nullstellensatz) which asserts that $\underline{a}^*$ is the radical of $\underline{a}$, that is to say it is the set of all polynomials f some power of which lies in $\underline{a}$. $V = V(S)$

is an <u>affine (k, K)-variety</u>.

Each polynomial f in k[t] determines a function $x \mapsto f(x)$ on K^n with values in K, and the restriction of this function to V is called a <u>regular function</u> on V. The regular functions form a ring A, clearly isomorphic to $k[t]/\underline{a}^*$; this ring is called the <u>coordinate ring</u> (or affine algebra) of V. Obviously A is finitely generated as a k-algebra, and from Hilbert's theorem it follows immediately that A has no non-zero nilpotent elements. Conversely, every finitely generated k-algebra A with no nilpotent elements $\neq 0$ arises as the coordinate ring of some (k, K)-variety V in K^n (for some n): we have only to take a set of generators $u_1, \ldots, u_n$ of A, which defines a k-algebra homomorphism of $k[t_1, \ldots, t_n]$ onto A; the kernel $\underline{a}$ of this homomorphism is an ideal which is equal to its own radical, and $V(\underline{a})$ is the variety sought. But there is a more intrinsic way of getting V from A: namely, the points of V are in one-to-one correspondence with the k-homomorphisms of A into K. For if $x \in V$, then $f \mapsto f(x)$ is a k-homomorphism $A \to K$; and conversely, if $\varphi : A \to K$ is a k-homomorphism, let $x_i = \varphi(u_i)$, then $x = (x_1, \ldots, x_n)$ is a point of V. Thus an affine algebraic variety is determined by its coordinate ring.

If U, V are affine (k, K)-varieties, say $U \subseteq K^m$, $V \subseteq K^n$, a mapping $f : U \to V$ is (k, K)-regular if it is induced by a k-polynomial mapping of K^m into K^n. We how have a category of affine varieties and regular maps (we shall drop the prefix (k, K) from now on). If A, B are the coordinate rings of U, V respectively, then the regular maps $f : U \to V$ correspond one-to-one to the k-algebra homomorphisms $\varphi : B \to A$: if $u \in B$ (i.e., $u : V \to K$ is regular) then $u \circ f : U \to K$ is regular and thus we have a mapping $u \mapsto u \circ f$ of B into A, which of course is a homomorphism. Moreover, this correspondence is functorial: if $g : V \to W$ corresponds to $\psi : C \to B$ (where C is the coordinate ring of W) then $g \circ f$ corresponds to $\varphi \circ \psi$. In this way it appears that the category of affine k-varieties is equivalent to the dual of the category of finitely-generated k-algebras with no nilpotent elements. In other words, the theory of affine algebraic varieties over k is equivalent to the theory of a rather special class of commutative rings, and one can compile a dictionary for translating statements about affine varieties into statements of commutative algebra. Thus, in the hands of the German school of the 1920's and

1930's, algebraic geometry became the study of ideals in polynomial rings.

THE ZARISKI TOPOLOGY

Let V be an affine k-variety, A its coordinate ring. The elements of A are functions from V to K. If S is any subset of A, let V(S) denote the set of common zeros of the functions in S; then it is easily verified that by taking the V(S) as closed sets we have a topology on V, called the Zariski topology (strictly, the k-topology). From the topologist's point of view, this is a very bad topology: in general it is not even T_0 (unless k = K, when it is T_1 (but not T_2)). If $x \in V$, the closure of the set $\{x\}$ in the Zariski topology is the intersection of all the closed sets V(S) which contain x: it is what Weil calls the locus of x, and its points are the specializations of x. Thus y is a specialization of x if and only if $y \in \overline{\{x\}}$.

PRODUCTS

If $U \subseteq K^m$, $V \subseteq K^n$ are two affine varieties then $U \times V \subseteq K^{m+n}$ is an affine variety, the product of U and V (it is the product of U and V in the category of all affine k-varieties, that is to say it satisfies the usual universal mapping property in this category). If A, B are the coordinate rings of U, V respectively then one might hope that the coordinate ring of U $\times$ V would be the tensor product $A \otimes_k B$. Unfortunately it isn't, in general, because $A \otimes_k B$ may well have nilpotent elements (unless k is perfect), and to get the coordinate ring of U $\times$ V one has to factor out the ideal of nilpotent elements in the tensor product. This is one example where the exclusion of nilpotent elements leads to an unsatisfactory situation.

It should also be remarked that the Zariski topology on U $\times$ V is not (in general) the product topology: generally it is strictly finer than the product topology, i.e. it has more open sets. The standard example is the affine plane K $\times$ K.

PROJECTIVE AND ABSTRACT VARIETIES

It was realised early on that affine geometry is in many respects unsatisfactory. For example, two subvarieties of an affine variety may have empty intersection even if their dimensions are right, and Bézout's theorem does not hold without qualification; or a point or subvariety may escape 'to infinity'. This was rectified by 'completing' affine space by sticking on suitable 'points at infinity', as everyone knows, and the result is projective space $P_n(K)$. From a geometrical point of view, projective space and projective varieties are much more satisfactory to deal with. The process outlined above of constructing coordinate rings etc. can be imitated in the projective case, but it doesn't work nearly as well. A projective variety V in $P_n(K)$ is given by a set of homogeneous polynomial equations $f_\alpha(x_0, x_1, \ldots, x_n) = 0$ (with coefficients in k); these generate a homogeneous ideal $\underline{a}$ in the graded polynomial ring $k[t_0, \ldots, t_n]$. The radical $\underline{a}^*$ of $\underline{a}$ is again a homogeneous ideal, so we can form $A = k[t]/\underline{a}^*$ which is a graded k-algebra. But: (i) the elements of A do not correspond to regular functions on V, because the only everywhere-defined regular functions on V are in fact constants; and (ii) there is no longer a one-to-one correspondence (as in the affine case) between graded coordinate rings and projective varieties: non-isomorphic rings can give rise to isomorphic varieties. For example, the coordinate ring of $P_1(K)$ and of a conic in $P_2(K)$ are not isomorphic.

A different approach is the following. $P_n(K)$ can be

regarded as the union of a finite number of overlapping affine spaces — for example, the complements of n + 1 hyperplanes with no common point — which are open sets in the Zariski topology, and hence any projective variety V is the union of a finite number of overlapping affine varieties U_i, which are open sets in V: thus V is 'locally affine'. The situation is analogous to that for a manifold, which is 'locally Euclidean', i.e., is obtained by sticking together overlapping Euclidian spaces in a suitable way. Thus it is natural to go further, as Weil did, and define an 'abstract variety' as one which is obtained by pasting together overlapping affine varieties. The resulting object may or may not be projective (i.e., embeddable in a projective space). The characteristic 'good' property of projective varieties, that they are in some sense 'compact' or that they don't have bits missing at infinity, is then replaced by the property of completeness, which can be formulated in various ways. Probably the simplest of these is the following: an (abstract) variety V is complete if, for every variety W, the projection $V \times W \to W$ is a closed map (with respect to the Zariski topology).

To give meaning to the definition of an abstract variety,

it is necessary to specify how the affine varieties which make it up are to be stuck together. There are various ways of doing this: one is the following. If V is an affine variety, say $V \subseteq K^n$, we associate with V a <u>structure sheaf</u> $\mathcal{O}_V$, which may be defined as follows. A <u>rational</u> function $u \in k(t_1, \ldots, t_n)$ is said to be <u>regular</u> at $x \in K^n$, or <u>defined</u> at x, if u can be put in the form f/g, where f, g are polynomials and $g(x) \neq 0$ (so that $u(x) = f(x)/g(x)$ is well-defined). The domain of definition of a rational function is an open set in K^n. A <u>rational function</u> u' <u>on</u> V is by definition the restriction to V of a rational function u on K^n (so the domain of u' is an open set in V). If U is any open set in V, the rational functions on V which are defined at every point of U form a ring A(U), and the assignment $U \mapsto A(U)$ is a presheaf of rings on V which is immediately verified to be a <u>sheaf</u>. This is the structure sheaf $\mathcal{O}_V$, and it is intrinsically related to V, i.e., it does not depend on the embedding of V in an affine space. One then defines a <u>prealgebraic variety</u> to be a topological space X together with a sheaf of rings $\mathcal{O}_X$, this sheaf being a sheaf of germs of functions on X with values in K, with the following property: there exists a finite open covering

$(V_i)_{1 \leqslant i \leqslant n}$ of X such that each V_i, together with the restriction of $\mathcal{O}_X$ to V_i, is isomorphic, sheaf and all, to an affine algebraic variety. X is an (abstract) algebraic variety if in addition it satisfies a 'separation axiom' which is the formal analogue of Hausdorff's axiom for topological spaces, namely that the diagonal should be a closed subset of the product $X \times X$ (only here, as we have already seen, the topology on $X \times X$ is not the product topology).

This definition is due to Serre (Faisceaux algébriques cohérents). Thus the philosophy is this: an affine variety is equivalent to a commutative ring (of a rather restricted type) and an abstract variety is obtained by sticking a number of these together by means of their structure sheaves.

We have now more or less set the stage. Going back for a moment to the affine case, we have remarked that any situation or theorem relating to affine varieties can be transcribed into one relating to their coordinate rings, and it has been recognised for a long time that in this way one gets more general statements, for generally the theorems of commutative algebra that arise are valid under much less restrictive hypotheses on the rings in question: often it is enough that they should be Noetherian. So, to obtain a satisfactorily general theory, one should start with a quite arbitrary commutative ring and construct something like an 'affine variety' from it, and then stick these objects together by means of structure sheaves to obtain generalised abstract varieties or *preschemes*.

Chapter 2

NOETHERIAN SPACES

A non-empty topological space X is said to be <u>irreducible</u> if every pair of non-empty open sets in X intersect (thus X is as far as possible from being Hausdorff). Equivalent conditions:

X is not the union of two proper closed subsets;

If F_i $(1 \leqslant i \leqslant n)$ are closed subsets which cover X, then $X = F_i$ for some i;

Every non-empty open set is dense in X;

Every open set in X is connected.

Examples. (1) Let X be an infinite set, and topologize X by taking the closed subsets to be X itself and all finite subsets of X. Then X is irreducible.

(2) Any irreducible algebraic variety, with the Zariski topology.

A subset Y of a space X is <u>irreducible</u> if Y is irreducible in the induced topology. The following facts are not hard to prove:

Proposition (2.1). (i) If $(F_i)_{1 \leqslant i \leqslant n}$ is a finite closed covering of a space X, and if Y is an irreducible subset of X, then $Y \subseteq F_i$ for some i.

(ii) If X is irreducible, every non-empty open subset of X is irreducible.

(iii) Let $(U_i)_{1 \leqslant i \leqslant n}$ be a finite open covering of a space X, the U_i being non-empty. Then X is irreducible $\Leftrightarrow$ each U_i is irreducible and meets each U_j.

(iv) If Y is a subset of X, then Y is irreducible if and only if $\bar{Y}$ is irreducible.

(v) The image of an irreducible set under a continuous map is irreducible.

(vi) X has maximal irreducible subsets; they are all closed and they cover X. (Use Zorn's lemma for (vi).)

The maximal irreducible subsets of X are called the irreducible components of X. Irreducibility is in some ways analogous to, but stronger than, connectedness.

If $x \in X$, then $\{x\}$ is irreducible and therefore (by (iv) above) so is $\overline{\{x\}}$. If V is an irreducible subset of X and $V = \overline{\{x\}}$ for some $x \in X$, then x is a <u>generic point</u> of V. If $y \in \overline{\{x\}}$, y is a <u>specialization</u> of x. The closed set $\overline{\{x\}}$ is the <u>locus</u> of x.

A subset Y of a space X is <u>locally closed</u> if Y is the intersection of an open set and a closed set in X, or equivalently if Y is open in its closure $\bar{Y}$, or equivalently again if every $y \in U$ has an open neighbourhood U_y in X such that $Y \cap U_y$ is closed in U_y.

A topological space X is <u>Noetherian</u> if the closed subsets of X satisfy the descending chain condition. Equivalent conditions:

The open sets in X satisfy the ascending chain condition;

Every open subset of X is quasi-compact (i.e., compact but not necessarily Hausdorff);

Every subset of X is quasi-compact.

Proposition (2.2). (i) A Noetherian space is quasi-compact.

(ii) Every subset of a Noetherian space (with the induced topology) is Noetherian.

(iii) Let X be a topological space and let $(X_i)_{1 \leqslant i \leqslant n}$ be a finite covering of X. If the X_i are Noetherian, then so is X.

(iv) If X is Noetherian, the number of irreducible components of X is <u>finite</u>.

The proofs are straightforward.

Chapter 3

THE SPECTRUM OF A COMMUTATIVE RING

Let A be a commutative ring with 1. Let X = Spec(A) denote the set of all prime ideals of A. ($\underline{p}$ is a prime ideal $\Leftrightarrow$ A/$\underline{p}$ is an integral domain; thus A itself is _not_ a prime ideal.) If $x \in X$ it is sometimes convenient to write j_x for the ideal x. For each subset E of A, let $V(E) = \{x \in X : j_x \supseteq E\}$. If E consists of a single element f, we write V(f) in place of $V(\{f\})$.

Lemma (3.1). (i) $V(0) = X$; $V(1) = \emptyset$.

(ii) If $E \subseteq E'$, then $V(E) \supseteq V(E')$.

(iii) $V(\bigcup_\lambda E_\lambda) = \bigcap_\lambda V(E_\lambda)$.

(iv) $V(EE') = V(E) \cup V(E')$.

Proof. Only (iv) is not entirely trivial. Clearly $V(EE') \supseteq V(E) \cup V(E')$. Conversely, if $x \notin V(E) \cup V(E')$ then there exist $f \in E$ and $f' \in E'$ such that $f \notin j_x$ and $f' \notin j_x$; since j_x is prime, we have $ff' \notin j_x$, hence $x \notin V(EE')$.

It follows from (3.1) that the sets V(E) satisfy the axioms for closed sets in a topology on X. This topology is called the Zariski topology or spectral topology on X, and it is the only one we shall use.

If $\underline{a}$ is an ideal in A, the radical $r(\underline{a})$ of $\underline{a}$ is the set of all $f \in A$ such that some power of f lies in $\underline{a}$; it is also the intersection of all the prime ideals of A which contain $\underline{a}$. In particular, the radical r(0) of the zero ideal is the set N of all nilpotent elements of A; this ideal is called the nilradical of A.

If E is a subset of A and if $\underline{a}$ is the ideal generated by E, then $V(E) = V(\underline{a}) = V(r(\underline{a}))$.

We need some more notation:

$A_x = A_{\underline{j}_x}$ = local ring of A with respect to the prime ideal $\underline{j}_x$;

$\underline{m}_x = \underline{j}_x A_x$ = maximal ideal of A_x;

$k(x) = A_x/\underline{m}_x$ = residue field of $A_x \cong$ field of fractions of $A/\underline{j}_x$.

If $f \in A$, f(x) denotes the class of f mod. $\underline{j}_x$ in $A/\underline{j}_x \subseteq k(x)$. Thus $f(x) = 0$ if and only if $f \in \underline{j}_x$.

$D(f) = X - V(f) = \{x \in X : f(x) \neq 0\}$ = 'support' of $f \in A$; it is an open set.

Finally, if $Y \subseteq X$, $\underline{j}(Y)$ denotes $\bigcap_{y \in Y} \underline{j}_y$. Thus $\underline{j}(\{x\}) = \underline{j}_x$. Then we have the following formulas:

Lemma (3.2). (i) $\underline{j}(\emptyset) = A$, $\underline{j}(X) = N$ (the nilradical of A).

(ii) If $Y \subseteq Y'$, then $\underline{j}(Y) \supseteq \underline{j}(Y')$.

(iii) $\underline{j}(\bigcup_\lambda Y_\lambda) = \bigcap_\lambda \underline{j}(Y_\lambda)$.

(iv) $\underline{j}(V(E))$ = radical of the ideal generated by E.

(v) $V(\underline{j}(Y)) = \bar{Y}$.

It follows from (iv) and (v) that $\underline{a} \mapsto V(\underline{a})$, $Y \mapsto \underline{j}(Y)$ gives an order-reversing one-one correspondence between closed subsets of X and ideals $\underline{a}$ in A such that $\underline{a} = r(\underline{a})$. Hence, if the ring A is Noetherian, X = Spec(A) is a Noetherian space. (The converse of this is false: X can be Noetherian and A not Noetherian. For example, let B be a polynomial ring $k[x_1, x_2, \ldots]$ over a field in a countable infinity of indeterminuates, let $\underline{b}$ be the ideal generated by $x_1, x_2^2, \ldots, x_n^n, \ldots$, and let $A = B/\underline{b}$. Then A is not Noetherian but has exactly one prime ideal.)

If $x, y \in X$ then $y \in \overline{\{x\}}$ (i.e., y is a specialization of x) if and only if $j_x \subseteq j_y$. Hence $\{x\}$ is a closed set (by abuse of language, x is a closed point of X) if and only if j_x is a maximal ideal of A. Thus X is a T_1 space (every point is closed) if and only if every ideal of A is maximal, i.e., dim A = 0. However, X is always a T_0-space (this means that, given any two distinct points x, y in X, then either there is a neighbourhood of y which does not contain x, or else a neighbourhood of x which does not contain y).

Next, let us look at the open sets D(f), $f \in A$. First, from (3.1) (iv) we have

$$D(fg) = D(f) \cap D(g) \quad (f, g \in A).$$

Proposition (3.3). (i) The open sets D(f) form a base of open sets for the topology of X.

(ii) Each D(f) is quasi-compact. In particular X = D(1) is quasi-compact.

Proof. (i) If U is an open set in X, then U = X - V(E) for some $E \subseteq A$; we have $V(E) = \bigcap_{f \in E} V(f)$ by (3.1) (iii), hence $U = \bigcup_{f \in E} D(f)$.

(ii) By virtue of (i) it is enough to show that every covering of a set D(f) by open sets $D(f_\lambda)$ has a finite subcovering.

Suppose then that $D(f) \subseteq \bigcup_{\lambda \in L} D(f_\lambda)$; let $\underline{a}$ be the ideal of A generated by the f_λ, then $V(f) \supseteq \bigcap V(f_\lambda) = V(\underline{a})$, hence $V(r(f)) \supseteq V(r(\underline{a}))$ and therefore $r(f) \subseteq r(\underline{a})$, so that $f \in r(\underline{a})$ and therefore $f^n \in \underline{a}$ for some $n > 0$. Say $f^n = \sum_{\lambda \in J} a_\lambda f_\lambda$, where J is some finite subset of L. Then $f^n \in \underline{b}$, where $\underline{b}$ is the ideal generated by the f_λ, $\lambda \in J$; hence $V(f) = V(f^n) \supseteq V(\underline{b}) = \bigcap_{\lambda \in J} V(f_\lambda)$. Taking complements, we have $D(f) \subseteq \bigcup_{\lambda \in J} D(f_\lambda)$, as required.

The open sets $D(f)$ $(f \in A)$ will be called basic open sets.

Let $\underline{a}$ be an ideal of A. Then the ideals of $A/\underline{a}$ correspond one-to-one to the ideals of A which contain $\underline{a}$, and therefore $\mathrm{Spec}(A/\underline{a})$ is canonically homeomorphic to the closed subspace $V(\underline{a})$ of Spec(A). In particular, Spec(A) and Spec(A/N) are canonically homeomorphic (N = nilradical of A).

Proposition (3.4). $X = \mathrm{Spec}(A)$ is irreducible $\Leftrightarrow$ A/N is an integral domain.

Proof. From what has just been said, we may as well take $N = 0$. Suppose X is reducible; then there exist proper closed subsets Y_1, Y_2 in X such that $Y_1 \cup Y_2 = X$, and therefore $\underline{i}(Y_1) \cap \underline{i}(Y_2) = \underline{i}(X) = N = 0$ (by (3.2)). But $\underline{i}(Y_1)$ and

$\underline{j}(Y_2)$ are $\neq 0$, hence there exist $f_i \in \underline{j}(Y_i)$ such that $f_i \neq 0$, and $f_1 f_2 \in \underline{j}(Y_1) \cap \underline{j}(Y_2) = 0$. Hence A is not an integral domain.

Conversely, if A is not an integral domain we have f, g in A such that $f \neq 0$, $g \neq 0$ and $fg = 0$. Hence $V(f) \neq X$, $V(g) \neq X$ (since $N = 0$); but $X = V(fg) = V(f) \cup V(g)$. Consequently X is reducible.

In the correspondence between closed subsets of X and ideals of A which are equal to their radicals, the irreducible closed subsets correspond to the prime ideals. In particular the irreducible <u>components</u> of X correspond to the <u>minimal</u> prime ideals of A. Furthermore, $x \mapsto \overline{\{x\}}$ gives a one-to-one correspondence between the points of X and the irreducible closed subsets of X, i.e., every irreducible closed subset of X has exactly one generic point. For if $x \in X$, then $\overline{\{x\}}$ is irreducible by (2.1) (iv). If $\overline{\{x\}} = \overline{\{y\}}$, then each of x and y is a specialization of the other, so that $\underline{j}_x = \underline{j}_y$, i.e. $x = y$. Conversely, if Y is an irreducible subset of X, Y corresponds to a prime ideal $\underline{j}_x$ of X, i.e. $Y = V(\underline{j}_x) = \overline{\{x\}}$.

COMPARISON WITH AFFINE ALGEBRAIC VARIETIES

Let k be a field, K an algebraically closed extension of k, and let V be a (k, K)-affine variety as in Chapter I; let A be the coordinate ring of V (a k-algebra, finitely generated with no nilpotent elements), and let $X = \text{Spec}(A)$. What is the relationship between V and X? Let us assume that K is a universal domain in the sense of Weil, i.e. that K has infinite transcendence degree over k; this is just to give us plenty of elbow room. Let $x \in V$, then x determines a homomorphism $A \to K$, whose kernel is a prime ideal of A, i.e. an element x' of X. Conversely, if $\underline{p}$ is any prime ideal of A, we can embed $A/\underline{p}$ in K (for the field of fractions of $A/\underline{p}$ is a finitely generated field extension of k, hence is an algebraic extension of a pure transcendental extension of k) and thus we have a homomorphism $A \to K$ with kernel $\underline{p}$. Hence $x \mapsto x'$ is a map of V onto X, and X is obtained from V by identifying 'equivalent' points in V, i.e. points which are generic specializations of each other.

At the other extreme, if $k = K$, then V may be identified with the set of maximal ideals of A, i.e. with the set of closed points of X: so in this case the map $V \to X$ described above is injective (and not in general surjective).

FUNCTORIAL PROPERTIES

Let A, A' be two rings and let $\varphi : A' \to A$ be a ring homomorphism (which is always assumed to map identity element to identity element). If $x \in X = \mathrm{Spec}(A)$, then $\varphi^{-1}(\underline{j}_x)$ is a prime ideal in A', hence a point of $X' = \mathrm{Spec}(A')$. Thus we have a mapping

$$\mathrm{Spec}(\varphi) = {}^a\varphi : X \to X',$$

said to be <u>associated</u> with φ. Let φ^x denote the embedding of $A'/\varphi^{-1}(\underline{j}_x)$ in A/j_x induced by φ; then φ^x extends to a field monomorphism

$$\varphi^x : k({}^a\varphi(x)) \to k(x).$$

Lemma (3.5). (i) ${}^a\varphi^{-1}(V(E')) = V(\varphi(E'))$, for any subset E' of A'. In particular:

(ii) ${}^a\varphi^{-1}(D(f')) = D(\varphi(f'))$ $(f' \in A')$.

(iii) ${}^a\varphi(V(\underline{a})) = V(\varphi^{-1}(\underline{a}))$ ($\underline{a}$ any ideal of A).

<u>Proof</u>. (i) is straightforward and (ii) follows from (i). To prove (iii) we may assume that $\underline{a} = r(\underline{a})$, since $V(r(\underline{a})) = V(\underline{a})$ and $r(\varphi^{-1}(\underline{a})) = \varphi^{-1}(r(\underline{a}))$. Put $Y = V(\underline{a})$, and let $\underline{a}' = \underline{j}({}^a\varphi(Y))$; then $V(\underline{a}') = \overline{{}^a\varphi(Y)}$ by (3.2) (v). Also:

$$f' \in \underline{a}' \Leftrightarrow f'(x') = 0 \text{ for all } x' \in {}^a\varphi(Y)$$

$$\Leftrightarrow f' \in \varphi^{-1}(\underline{j}_x) \text{ for all } x \in Y$$

$$\Leftrightarrow \varphi(f') \in j(Y) = j(V(\underline{a})) = \underline{a}$$

$$\Leftrightarrow f' \in \varphi^{-1}(\underline{a}).$$

Hence ${}^a\varphi(V(\underline{a})) = {}^a\varphi(Y) = V(\underline{a}') = V(\varphi^{-1}(\underline{a}))$.

From (i) or (ii) above it follows that ${}^a\varphi$ is continuous. Clearly, if A" is another ring, $\varphi' : A'' \to A'$ another ring homomorphism, then ${}^a(\varphi \circ \varphi') = {}^a\varphi' \circ {}^a\varphi$; so that Spec is a contravariant functor from the category of rings and ring homomorphisms to the category of topological spaces and continuous maps.

Examples. (1) If $\underline{a}$ is an ideal in A and $\varphi : A \to A/\underline{a}$ the projection, then ${}^a\varphi : \mathrm{Spec}(A/\underline{a}) \to \mathrm{Spec}(A)$ is a homeomorphism of $\mathrm{Spec}(A/\underline{a})$ onto $V(\underline{a})$.

(2) Let S be a multiplicatively closed subset of A (i.e. S is closed under finite products, so that in particular $1 \in S$ (take the empty product!)). Then we can form the ring of fractions $S^{-1}A$, and we have a canonical mapping $\varphi : A \to S^{-1}A$, hence ${}^a\varphi : \mathrm{Spec}(S^{-1}A) \to \mathrm{Spec}(A)$. It is a well-known and not difficult fact of commutative algebra that the prime ideals of $S^{-1}A$

are in one-one correspondence (under ${}^a\varphi$) with the prime ideals of A which don't meet S, and consequently ${}^a\varphi$ is a homeomorphism of $\mathrm{Spec}(S^{-1}A)$ onto the set of all $x \in X$ such that $\underline{j}_x \cap S = \emptyset$. (In general this subset of X is neither open nor closed, nor even locally closed.)

(3) In particular, $\mathrm{Spec}(A_x)$ may be canonically identified with the subspace of X consisting of all generizations of x, i.e. all y such that $x \in \overline{\{y\}}$.

(4) As another example, let $f \in A$ and let S be the set of all f^n $(n \geqslant 0)$. In this case $S^{-1}A$ is usually denoted by A_f. Then $\mathrm{Spec}(A_f)$ is identified with the set of all $x \in X$ such that $\underline{j}_x$ contains no power of f, i.e. such that $f \notin \underline{j}_x$. Hence

Proposition (3.6). If $\varphi : A \to A_f$ is the canonical homomorphism $(f \in A)$, then ${}^a\varphi$ is a homeomorphism of $\mathrm{Spec}(A_f)$ onto the open set $D(f)$.

(5) The 'characteristic morphism'. Since A has an identity element, there is a canonical mapping $\varphi : \underline{Z} \to A$, where $\underline{Z}$ is the ring of integers; hence ${}^a\varphi : X \to \mathrm{Spec}(\underline{Z})$. Now the points of $\mathrm{Spec}(\underline{Z})$ are (0) and the prime ideals (p) (p a positive prime number), and ${}^a\varphi(x)$ is just the ideal generated by the

characteristic of the residue field $k(x)$ of x.

Proposition (3.7). Let $\varphi : A' \to A$ be a ring homomorphism, ${}^a\varphi : X \to X'$ the associated map.

(i) If φ is surjective, ${}^a\varphi$ is a closed embedding (i.e. a homeomorphism of X onto a closed subset of X').

(ii) If φ is injective, ${}^a\varphi$ is dominant (i.e. ${}^a\varphi(X)$ is dense in X').

Proof. (i) is just Example 1 above.

(ii) follows from (3.5) (iii): $\overline{{}^a\varphi(X)} = \overline{{}^a\varphi(V(0))} = V(\varphi^{-1}(0)) = V(0)$ (since φ is injective) $= X'$.

Chapter 4

PRESHEAVES AND SHEAVES

PRESHEAVES AND SHEAVES

At this stage we need little more than the definitions. Let X be a topological space. A presheaf of abelian groups $\mathfrak{F}$ on X is the assignment of an abelian group $\mathfrak{F}(U)$ to each open set U in X, together with homomorphisms (often called restriction homomorphisms) $\mathfrak{F}(U) \to \mathfrak{F}(V)$ defined whenever $U \supseteq V$, such that $\mathfrak{F}(U) \to \mathfrak{F}(U)$ is the identity map, and that the composition $\mathfrak{F}(U) \to \mathfrak{F}(V) \to \mathfrak{F}(W)$ (where $U \supseteq V \supseteq W$) is the same as the homomorphism $\mathfrak{F}(U) \to \mathfrak{F}(W)$. (Think of the elements of $\mathfrak{F}(U)$ as functions on U.)

Another way of saying the same thing is as follows. Let $\underline{C}(X)$ be the category whose objects are the open sets in X and whose only morphisms are inclusions of open sets. Then a presheaf $\mathfrak{F}$ is just a contravariant functor from the category $\underline{C}(X)$ into the category (Ab) of abelian groups. Put this way, it is clear how to define a presheaf on X with values in any given category: for example, presheaves of rings, modules etc.

A presheaf $\mathfrak{F}$ is a sheaf if it satisfies the following condition:

For each open set U in X and each open covering (U_α) of U, and each family (s_α) such that $s_\alpha \in \mathfrak{F}(U_\alpha)$ and s_α, s_β have the same restriction to $\mathfrak{F}(U_\alpha \cap U_\beta)$ for all α, β, there is a unique $s \in \mathfrak{F}(U)$ whose restriction to U_α is s_α, for all α.

Another way of putting this is as follows. A diagram of sets and mappings

$$A \longrightarrow B \overset{v_1}{\underset{v_2}{\rightrightarrows}} C$$

is said to be exact if u maps A one-one onto the set of all $x \in B$ such that $v_1(x) = v_2(x)$. Then $\mathfrak{F}$ is a sheaf if and only if, for each open set U in X and each open covering (U_α) of U, the diagram

$$\mathfrak{F}(U) \longrightarrow \prod_\alpha \mathfrak{F}(U_\alpha) \rightrightarrows \prod_{\alpha,\beta} \mathfrak{F}(U_\alpha \cap U_\beta)$$

(in which the maps are products of restriction homomorphisms) is exact.

STALKS

Let $\mathfrak{F}$ be a presheaf (say of abelian groups) on X and let x be a point of X. Then the direct limit $\varinjlim \mathfrak{F}(U)$, where U runs through all open neighbourhoods of x in X, is called the stalk of $\mathfrak{F}$ at x and is denoted by $\mathfrak{F}_x$. Thus an element $s_x \in \mathfrak{F}_x$ is represented by some $s \in \mathfrak{F}(U)$, where U is some open neighbourhood of x in X, and two elements $s \in \mathfrak{F}(U)$ and $s' \in \mathfrak{F}(U')$ represent the same element of $\mathfrak{F}_x$ if and only if there is an open neighbourhood U" of x contained in $U \cap U'$ such that the restrictions of s and s' to U" are the same.

If U is any open set in X and if x is any point of U, we have a homomorphism $\mathfrak{F}(U) \to \mathfrak{F}_x$. If $s \in \mathfrak{F}(U)$ we denote the image of s under this homomorphism by s_x.

THE SHEAF ASSOCIATED WITH A PRESHEAF

Let $\mathfrak{F}$ be a presheaf on X and let E denote the disjoint union, or sum, of the stalks $\mathfrak{F}_x$; then E has a natural projection p onto X, namely the fibre $p^{-1}(x)$ is the stalk $\mathfrak{F}_x$ of $\mathfrak{F}$ at x. For each open set U in X and each $s \in \mathfrak{F}(U)$, let $\tilde{s}(x)$ denote s_x; then $\tilde{s} : U \to E$ is a section of E over U, i.e., $p \circ \tilde{s}$ is the identity map of U. We can make E into a topological space by giving E the coarsest topology for which all the mappings $\tilde{s}$ are continuous: this means that a set W is open in E if and only if, for each open $U \subseteq X$ and each $s \in \mathfrak{F}(U)$, the set of points $x \in U$ such that $\tilde{s}(x) \in W$ form an open set in X.

Let $\tilde{\mathfrak{F}}(U)$ denote the set of continuous sections of E over U. Then an element of $\tilde{\mathfrak{F}}(U)$ is a family $(s'_x)_{x \in U}$, where $s'_x \in \mathfrak{F}_x$ for all $x \in U$, such that for each $x \in U$ there is an open neighbourhood V of x, contained in U, and an element $x \in \mathfrak{F}(V)$ such that $s'_y = s_y$ for all $y \in V$. It is easily checked that

Lemma (4.1). $\tilde{\mathfrak{F}}$ is a <u>sheaf</u>.

If $\mathfrak{F}$, $\mathfrak{G}$ are presheaves on X, a <u>homomorphism</u> $\varphi : \mathfrak{F} \to \mathfrak{G}$ is a family of homomorphisms $\varphi(U) : \mathfrak{F}(U) \to \mathfrak{G}(U)$ for each open set U in X, which are compatible with the restriction homomorphisms in $\mathfrak{F}$ and $\mathfrak{G}$: that is, whenever U, V are open in X and $U \supseteq V$, the diagram

$$\begin{array}{ccc} \mathfrak{F}(U) & \xrightarrow{\varphi(U)} & \mathfrak{G}(U) \\ \downarrow & & \downarrow \\ \mathfrak{F}(V) & \xrightarrow[\varphi(V)]{} & \mathfrak{G}(V) \end{array}$$

(in which the vertical arrows are restrictions) is commutative.

If we regard $\mathfrak{F}$, $\mathfrak{G}$ as contravariant functors on the category $\underline{C}(X)$, then φ is just a morphism (or natural transformation) of functors.

In particular, let $\mathfrak{F}$ be a presheaf on X, $\widetilde{\mathfrak{F}}$ the associated sheaf (4.1). For each open set U in X and each $s \in \mathfrak{F}(U)$, the family $(s_x)_{x \in U}$ is an element of $\widetilde{\mathfrak{F}}(U)$, so that we have a homomorphism $\mathfrak{F} \to \widetilde{\mathfrak{F}}$.

Lemma (4.2). $\mathfrak{F} \to \widetilde{\mathfrak{F}}$ *is an isomorphism if and only if* $\mathfrak{F}$ *is a* sheaf.

If $\mathfrak{F}$ is a sheaf, we shall often use the notation $\Gamma(U, \mathfrak{F})$ instead of $\mathfrak{F}(U)$.

RESTRICTION OF A PRESHEAF TO AN OPEN SET

Let $\mathfrak{F}$ be a presheaf on X, and let U be an open set in X. Then the $\mathfrak{F}(V)$ for which $V \subseteq U$ form a presheaf on U, called the restriction of $\mathfrak{F}$ to U and denoted by $\mathfrak{F} \mid U$. If $\mathfrak{F}$ is a sheaf, so is $\mathfrak{F} \mid U$ (obvious from the definitions).

PRESHEAF ON A BASE OF OPEN SETS

We shall need a slight variant of the above notion of a presheaf. Let X be a topological space and let $\mathfrak{B}$ be a basis of open sets in X. A presheaf on $\mathfrak{B}$ (say a presheaf of abelian groups) is the assignment of an abelian group $\mathfrak{F}(U)$ to each $U \in \mathfrak{B}$, together with restriction homomorphisms $\mathfrak{F}(U) \to \mathfrak{F}(V)$ whenever $U, V \in \mathfrak{B}$ and $U \supseteq V$, satisfying the same conditions as before.

From a presheaf $\mathfrak{F}$ on $\mathfrak{B}$ we can construct a presheaf $\mathfrak{F}'$ on X in the previous sense: if U is any open set in X, then $\mathfrak{F}'(U)$ is defined to be the inverse limit $\varprojlim \mathfrak{F}(V)$, taken over all $V \in \mathfrak{B}$ such that $V \subseteq U$. Explicitly, an element $s' \in \mathfrak{F}(U)$ is a family $(s_V)_{V \in \mathfrak{B},\, V \subseteq U}$, such that if $V, W \in \mathfrak{B}$ and $U \supseteq V \supseteq W$, then the restriction of s_V to W is s_W. If $U \in \mathfrak{B}$, then $\mathfrak{F}'(U)$ is canonically isomorphic to $\mathfrak{F}(U)$.

Lemma (4.3). With the above notation, $\mathfrak{F}'$ is a sheaf on X if and only if $\mathfrak{F}$ satisfies the following condition: for each $U \in \mathfrak{B}$ and each covering (U_α) of U by sets belonging to $\mathfrak{B}$, the diagram

$$\mathfrak{F}(U) \to \prod_\alpha \mathfrak{F}(U_\alpha) \rightrightarrows \prod_{\alpha,\beta} \prod_{\substack{V \in \mathfrak{B} \\ V \subseteq U_\alpha \cap U_\beta}} \mathfrak{F}(V)$$

is exact: that is, if $s_\alpha \in \mathfrak{F}(U_\alpha)$ are such that the restrictions of s_α and s_β to V are the same, for all pairs α, β and all

$V \subseteq U_\alpha \cap U_\beta$ $(V \in \mathcal{B})$, then there is a unique $s \in \mathcal{F}(U)$ whose restriction to U_α is s_α for all α.

The stalk $\mathcal{F}'_x$ of $\mathcal{F}'$ at x is equal to $\varinjlim \mathcal{F}(U)$, where U runs through all sets of $\mathcal{B}$ which contain x, because these sets are cofinal in the set of all open neighbourhoods of x.

RINGED SPACES

A ringed space (espace annelé) is a pair $(X, \mathcal{O}_X)$ where X is a topological space and $\mathcal{O}_X$ is a sheaf of rings on X, called the structure sheaf of the ringed space.

Example. Let X be a complex manifold, and for each open set U in X let $\mathcal{O}(U)$ denote the ring of all holomorphic functions defined on U. Then $\mathcal{O}$ is a sheaf of rings on X, so that a complex manifold may be regarded as a ringed space $(X, \mathcal{O})$. Similarly for differentiable manifolds, algebraic varieties over a field, etc.

A morphism of ringed spaces $(X, \mathcal{O}_X) \to (Y, \mathcal{O}_Y)$ is a pair (ψ, θ), where ψ is a continuous map from X to Y, and θ maps $\mathcal{O}_Y$ to $\mathcal{O}_X$; precisely, θ assigns to each open set V in Y a ring homomorphism $\theta(V) : \Gamma(V, \mathcal{O}_Y) \to \Gamma(\psi^{-1}(V), \mathcal{O}_X)$, compatible with the restriction homomorphisms: that is to say, whenever $V \supseteq V'$ are open sets in Y, the diagram

$$\begin{array}{ccc} \Gamma(V, \mathcal{O}_Y) & \xrightarrow{\theta(V)} & \Gamma(\psi^{-1}(V), \mathcal{O}_X) \\ \downarrow & & \downarrow \\ \Gamma(V', \mathcal{O}_Y) & \xrightarrow[\theta(V')]{} & \Gamma(\psi^{-1}(V'), \mathcal{O}_X) \end{array}$$

is commutative. For each $x \in X$, θ then induces a homomorphism of the stalks

$$\theta_x^{\#} : \mathcal{O}_{Y, \psi(x)} \to \mathcal{O}_{X,x}$$

by taking direct limits.

Chapter 5

AFFINE SCHEMES

THE STRUCTURE SHEAF OF SPEC(A)

We shall put a sheaf of rings on $X = \mathrm{Spec}(A)$ (where A is any commutative ring) in such a way that the stalk of the sheaf at $x \in X$ is the local ring A_x (i.e. the local ring of A with respect to the prime ideal $\underline{j}_x$). For this we use the open sets $D(f)$ ($f \in A$) and the rings of fractions A_f (Chapter 3, Ex. 4 and Prop. (3.6)).

Suppose f, g in A are such that $D(f) \supseteq D(g)$. Then $r(f) \supseteq r(g)$, so that $g^n = sf$ for some $s \in A$ and some $n > 0$. Define a ring homomorphism

$$\rho_{g,f} : A_f \to A_g$$

as follows: $\rho_{g,f}(a/f^m) = as^m/g^{mn} \in A_g$. Verify that $\rho_{g,f}$ is a well-defined ring homomorphism depending only on f and g (and not on the particular equation $g^n = sf$ chosen), and that if $D(f) \supseteq D(g) \supseteq D(h)$ then $\rho_{h,g} \circ \rho_{g,f} = \rho_{h,f}$. Then the assignment $D(f) \mapsto A_f$ (and the homomorphisms $\rho_{g,f}$) forms a presheaf on the basis $\mathcal{B} = (D(f))_{f \in A}$. This presheaf on $\mathcal{B}$ determines a presheaf on X, denoted by $\mathcal{O}_X$ or by $\widetilde{A}$.

Proposition (5.1). (i) The stalk of $\mathcal{O}_X$ at $x \in X$ is isomorphic to A_x.

(ii) $\mathcal{O}_X$ is a sheaf on X, and hence $\Gamma(D(f), \mathcal{O}_X) \cong A_f$ for all $f \in A$. In particular $\Gamma(X, \mathcal{O}_X) \cong A$.

Proof. (i) is a straightforward verification: $x \in D(f)$ if and only if $f \notin j_x$, and $a/f^n \in A_f$ maps to $a/f^n \in A_{j_x} = A_x$. Check that this gives an isomorphism of $\varinjlim A_f$ onto A_x.

(ii) does require proof. We have to show that the condition of (4.3) is satisfied. First, by (3.6) D(f) is canonically homeomorphic to $\mathrm{Spec}(A_f)$; also it is easily checked that the presheaf $\widetilde{A_f}$ on $\mathrm{Spec}(A_f)$ constructed as above is canonically isomorphic to $\widetilde{A} \mid D(f)$. Hence it is enough to show that $\Gamma(X, \mathcal{O}_X) = A$, i.e. that if $(D(f_i))_{i \in I}$ is any covering of X by basic open sets, and if $s_i \in A_{f_i}$ are such that the images of s_i, s_j in A_g are the same for all $g \in A$ such that $D(g) \subseteq D(f_i) \cap D(f_j)$, then there exists a unique $s \in A$ whose image in A_{f_i} is s_i, for all $i \in I$.

Uniqueness: if s, $s' \in A$ are solutions of this problem, then $t = s - s'$ has zero image in each A_{f_i}, hence for each $i \in I$ we have $tf_i^{n_i} = 0$ for some $n_i > 0$. Since the $D(f_i)$ cover X and since $D(f_i) = D(f_i^{n_i})$, the ideal generated by the $f_i^{n_i}$ is the whole of A. Consequently we have an equation of the form $1 = \Sigma a_i f_i^{n_i}$ $(a_i \in A)$, and hence $t = \Sigma a_i t f_i^{n_i} = 0$. Therefore $s = s'$.

Existence: X is quasi-compact by (3.3), hence there is a _finite_ subset J of I such that $X = \bigcup_{i \in J} D(f_i)$. Say $s_i = z_i/f_i^{m_i}$ $(i \in J)$, where $z_i \in A$. Since J is finite we may suppose that all the m_i are equal: say $s_i = z_i/f_i^m$ $(i \in J)$. For each pair i, j in J the images of s_i and s_j in $A_{f_i f_j}$ are the same, so that

$$z_i f_j^m/(f_i f_j)^m = z_j f_i^m/(f_i f_j)^m \quad \text{in } A_{f_i f_j},$$

i.e.

$$(z_i f_j^m - z_j f_i^m)(f_i f_j)^{m_{ij}} = 0 \quad \text{in } A,$$

for some integer m_{ij}. Again, we may assume that all the m_{ij} are equal, say $m_{ij} = n$ for all $i, j \in J$; then, multiplying each z_i by f_i^n, we reduce to the case $n = 0$, i.e.

$$z_i f_j^m = z_j f_i^m.$$

Now the $D(f_i) = D(f_i^m)$ $(i \in J)$ cover X, hence the ideal generated by the f_i^m is the whole of A, so that we have an equation of the form

$$1 = \sum_{i \in J} g_i f_i^m \quad (g_i \in A).$$

Put $s_J = \sum_{i \in J} g_i z_i$; then

$$s_J f_j^m = \sum_i g_i z_i f_j^m = \sum_i g_i z_j f_i^m = z_j \quad \text{in } A,$$

so that the image of s_J in A_{f_j} is $a_j/f_j^m = s_j$ (for all $j \in J$). On the face of it, s_J depends on the finite subset J; but if $J' \supseteq J$ is another finite subset of I, we construct $s_{J'}$ satisfying the same conditions as s_J, and by the uniqueness of the solution $s_{J'}$ must therefore be equal to s_J.

Thus, starting from an arbitrary commutative ring A, we have constructed a topological space X = Spec(A) and a sheaf of local rings $\mathcal{O}_X$ (or $\widetilde{A}$) on X. This is the basic construction on which all else is founded. The ringed space $(X, \mathcal{O}_X)$ is called the affine scheme of the ring A.

MORPHISMS OF AFFINE SCHEMES

Let A, B be rings, X = Spec(A), Y = Spec(B), and let $\varphi : B \to A$ be a ring homomorphism. We have seen in Chapter 3 that φ defines an associated continuous mapping ${}^a\varphi : X \to Y$. In fact φ defines a morphism of ringed spaces

$({}^a\varphi, \tilde{\varphi}) : (X, \mathcal{O}_X) \to (Y, \mathcal{O}_Y)$, as follows. Let $g \in B$, then $D(g)$ is a basic open set in Y, and we have ${}^a\varphi^{-1}(D(g)) = D(\varphi(g))$ by (3.5). How φ induces a homomorphism $B_g \to A_{\varphi(g)}$, namely b/g^n is mapped to $\varphi(b)/\varphi(g)^n$; hence by (5.1) (ii) φ induces a homomorphism

$$\tilde{\varphi}_{D(g)} : \Gamma(D(g), \mathcal{O}\ ) \to \Gamma({}^a\varphi^{-1}(D(g)), \mathcal{O}_X).$$

Clearly the $\tilde{\varphi}_{D(g)}$ are compatible with the restriction homomorphisms, hence we have $\tilde{\varphi} : \mathcal{O}_Y \to \mathcal{O}_X$ as required. $\tilde{\varphi}$ induces a homomorphism of the stalks: if $y = {}^a\varphi(x)$, we have $\tilde{\varphi}_x^{\#} : \mathcal{O}_{Y,y} \to \mathcal{O}_{X,x}$. Now $\mathcal{O}_{Y,y} \cong B_y$, $\mathcal{O}_{X,x} \cong A_x$, and the map $B_y \to A_x$ is the obvious one: $b/s \in B_y$ is mapped to $\varphi(b)/\varphi(s) \in A_x$.

If P, Q are local rings, $\underline{m}$ and $\underline{n}$ their respective maximal ideals, a homomorphism $f : P \to Q$ is said to be <u>local</u> if the following equivalent conditions are satisfied:

(i) $f(\underline{m}) \subseteq \underline{n}$ (i.e. the image of a non-unit is a non-unit);

(ii) $f^{-1}(\underline{n}) = \underline{m}$ (i.e. the inverse image of a unit is a unit).

If so, then f induces a field monomorphism $P/\underline{m} \to Q/\underline{n}$.

Now in the case in point, the homomorphism $B_y \to A_x$ is <u>local</u>, for the maximal ideal of A_x is $\underline{j}_x A_x$ and that of B_y is $\underline{j}_y B_y = \varphi^{-1}(\underline{j}_x)A_x$. Hence the morphism

$({}^a\varphi, \widetilde{\varphi}) : (X, \mathcal{O}_X) \to (Y, \mathcal{O}_Y)$ has the property that the homomorphisms induced on the stalks are <u>local</u> homomorphisms.

Conversely, let $(\psi, \theta) : (X, \mathcal{O}_X) \to (Y, \mathcal{O}_Y)$ be a morphism of ringed spaces (where $X = \mathrm{Spec}(A)$, $Y = \mathrm{Spec}(B)$ and $\mathcal{O}_X$, $\mathcal{O}_Y$ are the structure sheaves $\widetilde{A}$, $\widetilde{B}$) such that $\theta_x^{\#} : B_y \to A_x$ is a <u>local</u> homomorphism for each $x \in X$ $(y = \psi(x))$. We have then, in particular, a ring homomorphism $\theta(Y) : \Gamma(Y, \mathcal{O}_Y) \to \Gamma(X, \mathcal{O}_X)$; but $\Gamma(Y, \mathcal{O}_Y) \cong B$ and $\Gamma(X, \mathcal{O}_X) \cong A$ by (5.1), hence (ψ, θ) determines a ring homomorphism $\varphi : B \to A$. Since $\theta_x^{\#}$ is local, it gives rise to an embedding

$$\theta^x : k(y) \to k(x)$$

of the residue fields, such that for each $g \in B$ we have $\theta^x(g(y)) = \varphi(g)(x)$. Since θ^x is injective we have $g(y) = 0$ if and only if $\varphi(g)(x) = 0$, i.e. $g \in \mathfrak{j}_y$ if and only if $\varphi(g) \in \mathfrak{j}_x$, so that $\mathfrak{j}_y = \varphi^{-1}(\mathfrak{j}_x)$, i.e. $y = {}^a\varphi(x)$; hence $\psi = {}^a\varphi$. Moreover, the diagram

$$\begin{array}{ccc} B & \xrightarrow{\varphi} & A \\ \downarrow & & \downarrow \\ B_y & \xrightarrow[\theta_x^{\#}]{} & A_x \end{array}$$

is commutative, hence $\theta_x^{\#}$ is the homomorphism of B_y into A_x induced by φ; but θ is uniquely determined by the homomorphisms $\theta_x^{\#}$, and therefore $(\psi, \theta) = ({}^a\varphi, \widetilde{\varphi})$. We have therefore proved

Proposition (5.2). There is a one-to-one correspondence between the ring homomorphisms $B \to A$ and the morphisms $(\psi, \theta) : (X, \mathcal{O}_X) \to (Y, \mathcal{O}_Y)$ such that $\theta_x^{\#}$ is a local homomorphism for each $x \in X$.

So far, this is the basic local theory. The next step is to define the global objects. By analogy with Serre's definition of an algebraic variety (Chapter 1), it is clear what the general definition should be.

Chapter 6

PRESCHEMES

If $(X, \mathcal{O}_X)$ is a ringed space, an open subset V of X is said to be an affine open set if the ringed space $(V, \mathcal{O}_X|V)$ is isomorphic to some affine scheme.

Definition. A *prescheme* is a ringed space $(X, \mathcal{O}_X)$ such that every $x \in X$ has an affine open neighbourhood, i.e., it is a *locally affine* ringed space.

Let $(X, \mathcal{O}_X)$ be a prescheme.

Lemma (6.1). (i) The affine open sets form a basis of the topology of X.

(ii) If U is any open set in X, the ringed space $(U, \mathcal{O}_X|U)$ is a prescheme, called the *restriction* of $(X, \mathcal{O}_X)$ to U.

(iii) X is a T_0-space.

(iv) Every irreducible closed subset F of X has a unique generic point x, and $x \mapsto \overline{\{x\}}$ is a one-one correspondence between the points of X and the irreducible closed subsets of X.

Proofs. (i) Let U be an open set in X, and for each $x \in U$ let V_x be an affine open neighbourhood of x; then U is the union of the sets $U_x = U \cap V_x$; each U_x is open in V_x and is therefore a union of basic open sets contained in V_x, by (3.3); and these basic open sets are affine by (5.1). Hence U is a union of affine open sets.

(ii) follows from (i).

(iii) Let $x, y \in X$, $x \neq y$. If x and y are not in the same affine open set, it is clear that the T_0 condition is satisfied. If they are in the same affine open set, use the fact (Chapter 3) that an affine scheme is a T_0-space.

(iv) Let $y \in F$ and let U be an affine open neighbourhood of y in X. Then $U \cap F$ is dense in F (since F is irreducible) and is itself irreducible, hence is the closure in U of some $x \in U$. Hence if $F' = \overline{\{x\}}$ is the closure of $\{x\}$ in X, we have $F' \subseteq F$ (since $x \in F$); but $U \cap F' = U \cap F$, hence $U \cap (F' - F) = \emptyset$, hence $F' - F = \emptyset$ since F' is irreducible. Hence $F = \overline{\{x\}}$. The uniqueness of the generic point follows from (iii), for the T_0-axiom is equivalent to the statement: $\overline{\{x\}} = \overline{\{y\}} \Rightarrow x = y$.

MORPHISMS OF PRESCHEMES

Let $(X, \mathcal{O}_X)$ and $(Y, \mathcal{O}_Y)$ be preschemes. A morphism of ringed spaces $(\psi, \theta) : (X, \mathcal{O}_X) \to (Y, \mathcal{O}_Y)$ is a *morphism of preschemes* if, for each $x \in X$, $\theta_x^{\#}$ is a *local* homomorphism $\mathcal{O}_{Y, \psi(x)} \to \mathcal{O}_{X, x}$. Hence $\theta_x^{\#}$ defines a field monomorphism $\theta^x : k(\psi(x)) \to k(x)$, so that $k(x)$ is an *extension* of the field $k(\psi(x))$.

RELATIVE THEORY: S-PRESCHEMES

Let S be a fixed prescheme. (Strictly speaking, we should write $(S, \mathcal{O}_S)$, but from now on we shall drop the structure sheaf from the notation.) An *S-prescheme* is a pair (X, f), where X is a prescheme and $f : X \to S$ is a morphism of preschemes. If S is the affine scheme of a ring A, we speak of an *A-prescheme*.

If (X, f) and (Y, g) are S-preschemes, an *S-morphism* $\varphi : X \to Y$ is a morphism of preschemes such that the diagram

$$\begin{array}{ccc} X & \xrightarrow{\varphi} & Y \\ & {}_{f}\searrow \quad \swarrow_{g} & \\ & S & \end{array}$$

is commutative.

The 'base prescheme' S may be considered as a

generalization of the ground field of algebraic geometry: if A is the coordinate ring of an affine k-variety, then A is a k-algebra with identity element, so we have a homomorphism $k \to A$, hence $\mathrm{Spec}(A) \to \mathrm{Spec}(k)$. Thus Spec(A) is a k-prescheme. (Of course, Spec(k) consists of only one point, so the map $\mathrm{Spec}(A) \to \mathrm{Spec}(k)$ is trivial as a map of topological spaces; but a morphism of preschemes comprises also a map of the structure sheaves.)

Every prescheme may be considered canonically as a $\underline{Z}$-prescheme. Namely the 'characteristic morphism' (Ex. 5, Chapter 3) is a morphism $\mathrm{Spec}(A) \to \mathrm{Spec}(\underline{Z})$, and hence one defines a morphism of preschemes $X \to \mathrm{Spec}(\underline{Z})$ for any prescheme X (do it on the affine open sets).

PRODUCTS

Let $\underline{C}$ be any category and for any two objects X, T in $\underline{C}$, let X(T) denote the set of all morphisms $T \to X$ in $\underline{C}$. For fixed X and variable T, $T \mapsto X(T)$ is a contravariant functor $\underline{C} \to$ (Sets) (= category of all sets).

Let F be any contravariant functor on $\underline{C}$ with values in (Sets). F is said to be <u>representable</u> if there exists an object

X in $\underline{C}$ and a functorial isomorphism $F(T) \cong X(T)$ (for all $T \in \underline{C}$). If X exists, it must be unique up to isomorphism.

A product of two objects X, Y in $\underline{C}$ is an object $X \times Y$ which (if it exists) represents the functor $T \mapsto X(T) \times Y(T)$: in other words, there is a functorial isomorphism $(X \times Y)(T) \cong X(T) \times Y(T)$ for all objects T in $\underline{C}$.

Products exist in many categories: in the category of groups ('direct products'), topological spaces, algebraic varieties, modules over a fixed ring (here the product is 'direct sum' $M \oplus N$), etc. The dual concept is that of sum: in the category of groups, for example, sum is 'free product'; in the category of commutative A-algebras, where A is a fixed commutative ring, sum is tensor product over A. Since the category of affine schemes over A is dual to the category of A-algebras, $\mathrm{Spec}(B \otimes_A C)$ is a product of Spec(B) and Spec(C) in the category of affine schemes over A (here B, C are any two A-algebras).

Theorem (6.2). Let S be a fixed prescheme, X and Y two S-preschemes. Then the product $X \times_S Y$ exists in the category of S-preschemes.

The proof is tedious but not essentially difficult (EGA, I, 3.2.6), and we shall not reproduce it here. Locally, as we have just observed, it corresponds to the tensor product of rings, and it is a question of sticking things together so that it all fits.

This product of course has the usual associativity and commutativity properties, as in any category in which products exist.

The existence of products is fundamental, and arises in many contexts:

(1) Change of base. If X is an S-prescheme and if $S' \to S$ is a morphism of preschemes, then the product $X \underset{S}{\times} S'$ is denoted by $X_{(S')}$ and is said to be obtained by extension of the base-prescheme from S to S'. We have a commutative diagram

$$\begin{array}{ccc} X & \longleftarrow & X_{(S')} \\ \downarrow & & \downarrow \\ S & \longleftarrow & S' \end{array}$$

and $X_{(S')}$ is to be regarded as an S'-prescheme.

Base extension is a transitive operation, i.e. if $S'' \to S' \to S$ are morphisms of preschemes and X is an

S-prescheme, then $(X \times_S S') \times_{S'} S''$ is canonically isomorphic to $X \times_S S''$.

This operation generalizes the notion of extension of the ground-field in algebraic geometry: if X is a k-variety, say affine with coordinate ring A, and if k' is an extension field of k, then the embedding $k \to k'$ gives $\mathrm{Spec}(k') \to \mathrm{Spec}(k)$, and $A \otimes_k k'$ gives rise to an affine variety $X_{k'}$, defined over k'.

(2) Geometrical points. If X is an affine (k, K)-variety (Chapter I) with coordinate ring A, then the points of X are in one-one correspondence with the k-homomorphisms $A \to K$, i.e. with the k-morphisms $\mathrm{Spec}(K) \to \mathrm{Spec}(A)$. This motivates the following definition: if X, T are S-preschemes, the S-morphisms $T \to X$ are called points of the S-prescheme X with values in the S-prescheme T. Let $X(T)_S$ denote the set of points of X with values in T, then the product of two S-preschemes X and Y is characterized by the formula

$(X \times_S Y)(T)_S = X(T)_S \times Y(T)_S$, for any S-prescheme T.

In particular, a geometrical point of X is a point of X with values in an algebraically closed field K, that is to say it is a morphism $\varphi : \mathrm{Spec}(K) \to X$. Spec(K) consists of a single point, whose image under φ is the locality of the geometrical point. Given the locality x, the geometrical point φ is determined by an embedding of the residue field k(x) in K.

Remark. The product $X \times_S Y$ is not the set-theoretic product of X and Y, nor even the fibre product of X and Y over S: that is to say, if (X) temporarily denotes the set underlying X, then in general we have $(X \times_S Y) \neq (X) \times_{(S)} (Y)$. However, there is a surjective mapping $f : (X \times_S Y) \to (X) \times_{(S)} (Y)$. For if $x \in X$ and $y \in Y$ lie over the same point $s \in S$, then k(x) and k(y) are extensions of k(s), and can therefore both be embedded in an extension K of k(s); hence we have S-morphisms $\mathrm{Spec}(K) \to X$ and $\mathrm{Spec}(K) \to Y$, localized at x and y respectively, and therefore an S-morphism $\mathrm{Spec}(K) \to X \times Y$, localized at say z. Clearly the projections of z are x and y, i.e. f(z) = (x, y).

To show that f is not in general injective, it is enough to take X, Y, S to be the spectra of fields K, L, k respectively (K, L being extensions of k); then $K \otimes_k L$ in general has more than one prime ideal.

In fact it is not difficult to show that if $x \in X$ and $y \in Y$ lie over the same point $s \in S$, then the points z of $Z \times_S Y$ such that f(z) = (x, y) are in one-one correspondence with the isomorphism types of composite extensions of k(x) and k(y) over k(s) (E.G.A. I, 3.4.9).

(3) Fibres. Let $f : X \to Y$ be a morphism of preschemes and let y be a point of Y. Then the projection $p : X \times_Y \mathrm{Spec}(k(y)) \to X$ is a homeomorphism of the space underlying $X \times_Y \mathrm{Spec}(k(y))$ onto the fibre $f^{-1}(y)$ (E.G.A., I, 3.6.1). Hence the fibre $f^{-1}(y)$ can be regarded as a prescheme over the field k(y): as such we denote it by X_y. If $x \in f^{-1}(y)$ and $p(x') = x$, where $x' \in X \times_Y \mathrm{Spec}(k(y))$, it turns out that the residue fields k(x) and k(x') are the same, i.e. the residue field k(x) is the same whether x is regarded as a point of the prescheme X or as a point of the prescheme X_y.

(4) Separated morphisms. Schemes. Whenever the product $X \times X$ is defined in a category $\underline{C}$ (X being an object of $\underline{C}$), there is a well defined diagonal morphism $\Delta_X : X \to X \times X$. Δ_X is the element of $(X \times X)(X)$ corresponding to (id_X, id_X) in $X(X) \times X(X)$ (id_X = identity morphism of X). Hence if $f : X \to X$ is a morphism of preschemes, we have a diagonal morphism $\Delta_{X|S} : X \to X \times_S X$. If $X = \mathrm{Spec}(A)$, $S = \mathrm{Spec}(B)$ then Δ corresponds to the homomorphism $A \otimes_B A \to A$ which maps $x \otimes y$ to xy; this homomorphism is surjective and therefore Δ is in this case a homeomorphism of X onto a closed subset of the product.

If X, S are arbitrary preschemes, let $p_1 : X \times_S X \to X$ be the projection on the first factor; then $p_1 \circ \Delta$ is the identity map of X and therefore Δ is a homeomorphism of X onto $\Delta(X)$. If (U_α) is a covering of X by affine open sets, then $\Delta(X) \cap (U_\alpha \times U_\alpha)$ is the diagonal of $U_\alpha \times U_\alpha$, hence closed in $U_\alpha \times U_\alpha$; and $\Delta(X)$ is contained in $\bigcup_\alpha (U_\alpha \times U_\alpha)$, hence $\Delta(X)$ is locally closed (Chapter 2) (but not necessarily closed) in $X \times X$.

The morphism $f : X \to S$ is said to be separated, or X is separated over S, if $\Delta(X)$ is closed in $X \times_S X$.

A prescheme X is a scheme if it is separated over $\underline{Z}$, i.e. if the 'characteristic morphism' $X \to \mathrm{Spec}(\underline{Z})$ is separated. This is the formal analogue of Hausdorff's axiom, or of Serre's second axiom for algebraic varieties (see Chapter 1).

Remark. If $X = \mathrm{Spec}(A)$, then $A \otimes_{\underline{Z}} A \to A$ is surjective, as we have remarked above, and therefore the characteristic morphism $X \to \mathrm{Spec}(\underline{Z})$ is separated. This justifies the terminology 'affine scheme' rather than 'affine prescheme'.

If U, V are two affine open sets in a prescheme X, then $U \cap V$ need not be affine. But if X is a scheme, $U \cap V$ will be affine, for $U \cap V$ is isomorphic to $\Delta(X) \cap (U \times_{\underline{Z}} V)$, hence is closed in $U \times_{\underline{Z}} V$ and therefore affine.

(5) Proper morphisms. A morphism of preschemes $f : X \to S$ is of finite type if S is a union of affine open sets V_α such that each $f^{-1}(V_\alpha)$ is a finite union of affine open sets $U_{i\alpha}$ with the property that each ring $A(U_{i\alpha})$ is finitely generated as an algebra over $A(V_\alpha)$ (here, if U is an affine scheme, $A(U)$ denotes the associated ring). If X and S are both affine, say $X = \mathrm{Spec}(A)$, $S = \mathrm{Spec}(B)$, then $f : X \to S$ is of finite type if and only if A is finitely generated as a B-algebra (E.G.A., I, 6.3.3).

A morphism $f : X \to S$ is proper if

(i) f is separated and of finite type;

(ii) f is universally closed, i.e. for every morphism $S' \to S$ the projection $X_{(S')} = X \times_S S' \to S'$ is a closed mapping.

This is the generalization of the notion of completeness for an algebraic variety over a field (cf. Chapter I).

Chapter 7

OPERATIONS ON SHEAVES. QUASI-COHERENT AND COHERENT SHEAVES

Let $(X, \mathfrak{O})$ be a ringed space. An $\mathfrak{O}$-Module (note the capital M) is a sheaf $\mathfrak{F}$ of abelian groups such that, for each open set U in X, the group $\mathfrak{F}(U)$ carries a structure of an $\mathfrak{O}(U)$-module, these structures being compatible with the restriction homomorphisms: explicitly, if $U \supseteq V$ are open sets in X, then the restriction $\varphi : \mathfrak{F}(U) \to \mathfrak{F}(V)$ is compatible with the restriction $\rho : \mathfrak{O}(U) \to \mathfrak{O}(V)$, that is to say, if $f \in \mathfrak{F}(U)$ and $a \in \mathfrak{O}(U)$ then $\varphi(af) = \rho(a) . \varphi(f)$. Then each stalk $\mathfrak{F}_x$ has a natural $\mathfrak{O}_x$-module structure, defined as follows: if $a_x \in \mathfrak{O}_x$, $f_x \in \mathfrak{F}_x$, say a_x is the image of $a \in \mathfrak{O}(U)$, f_x the image of $f \in \mathfrak{F}(U)$ for some sufficiently small open neighbourhood U of x; then $a_x . f_x$ is the image of af in $\mathfrak{F}_x$.

In particular, $\mathfrak{O}$ itself is an $\mathfrak{O}$-Module.

Most of the concepts of module theory have their counterparts for Modules:—

(i) An <u>$\mathcal{O}$-Module homomorphism</u> $\varphi : \mathfrak{F} \to \mathfrak{G}$ is a sheaf homomorphism (i.e. a family of homomorphisms $\varphi(U) : \mathfrak{F}(U) \to \mathfrak{G}(U)$, commuting with the restrictions) such that each $\varphi(U)$ is an $\mathcal{O}(U)$-module homomorphism. Then each $\varphi_x : \mathfrak{F}_x \to \mathfrak{G}_x$ is an $\mathcal{O}_x$-module homomorphism.

(ii) <u>Sub-Modules</u>. A subsheaf $\mathfrak{F}'$ of an $\mathcal{O}$-Module $\mathfrak{F}$ is a sub-Module of $\mathfrak{F}$ if, for each open set U in X, $\mathfrak{F}'(U)$ is a sub-$\mathcal{O}(U)$-module of $\mathfrak{F}(U)$. Then each $\mathfrak{F}'_x$ is a sub-$\mathcal{O}_x$-module of $\mathfrak{F}_x$, and the embedding $\mathfrak{F}' \to \mathfrak{F}$ is an $\mathcal{O}$-Module homomorphism. In particular, a sub-Module of $\mathcal{O}$ is called an Ideal (with a capital I).

(iii) <u>Quotient Modules</u>. Let $\mathfrak{F}$ be an $\mathcal{O}$-Module, $\mathfrak{F}'$ a sub-Module of $\mathfrak{F}$. For each open set U in X, form $\mathfrak{F}(U)/\mathfrak{F}'(U)$. $U \mapsto \mathfrak{F}(U)/\mathfrak{F}'(U)$, with the induced restriction homomorphisms, is a presheaf, but <u>not</u> necessarily a sheaf. So we form the sheaf associated with this presheaf: this is the quotient Module $\mathfrak{F}'' = \mathfrak{F}/\mathfrak{F}'$. Since $\varinjlim$ is exact, we have $\mathfrak{F}''_x = \mathfrak{F}_x/\mathfrak{F}'_x$.

(iv) <u>Kernel</u>. Let $\varphi : \mathfrak{F} \to \mathfrak{G}$ be an $\mathcal{O}$-Module homomorphism. For each open set U in X let $\mathfrak{F}'(U)$ be the kernel of $\varphi(U) : \mathfrak{F}(U) \to \mathfrak{G}(U)$. Then $U \mapsto \mathfrak{F}'(U)$ is a <u>sheaf</u> $\mathfrak{F}'$, called the <u>kernel</u> of φ. Clearly $\mathfrak{F}'$ is an $\mathcal{O}$-Module. We have

$\mathfrak{F}'_x = \operatorname{Ker}(\varphi_x)$ for all $x \in X$.

(v) Image. For each open set U in X we can form $\operatorname{Im}(\varphi(U))$, which is a submodule of $\mathfrak{G}(U)$. $U \mapsto \operatorname{im}(\varphi(U))$ is a presheaf (not necessarily a sheaf). Let $\mathfrak{H}$ be the sheaf associated with this presheaf. Then $\mathfrak{H}$ is a subsheaf of $\mathfrak{G}$, called the image of $\mathfrak{G}$. Again by the exactness of $\varinjlim$ we have $\mathfrak{H}_x = \operatorname{Im}(\varphi_x)$. Also $\mathfrak{H}$ is isomorphic to the quotient $\mathfrak{F}/\mathfrak{F}'$, where $\mathfrak{F}'$ is the kernel of φ.

(vi) Cokernel. The cokernel of φ is $\mathfrak{G}/\mathfrak{H}$. We have the formulas

$$(\operatorname{Ker}(\varphi))_x \cong \operatorname{Ker}(\varphi_x); \quad (\operatorname{Im}(\varphi))_x \cong \operatorname{Im}(\varphi_x);$$
$$(\operatorname{Coker}(\varphi))_x \cong \operatorname{Coker}(\varphi_x).$$

The class of $\mathfrak{G}$-Modules is an abelian category. Exact sequences are defined in the usual way.

Lemma (7.1). A sequence $\mathfrak{F} \xrightarrow{\varphi} \mathfrak{G} \xrightarrow{\psi} \mathfrak{H}$ is exact if and only if $\mathfrak{F}_x \xrightarrow{\varphi_x} \mathfrak{G}_x \xrightarrow{\psi_x} \mathfrak{H}_x$ is exact for all $x \in X$.

Proof. $\mathfrak{F} \to \mathfrak{G} \to \mathfrak{H}$ is exact $\Leftrightarrow \operatorname{Im}(\varphi) = \operatorname{Ker}(\psi) \Leftrightarrow (\operatorname{Im}(\varphi))_x = (\operatorname{Ker}(\psi))_x$ for all $x \in X \Leftrightarrow \operatorname{Im}(\varphi_x) = \operatorname{Ker}(\psi_x)$ for all $x \in X$ $\Leftrightarrow \mathfrak{F}_x \to \mathfrak{G}_x \to \mathfrak{H}_x$ is exact for all $x \in X$.

Lemma (7.2). The "section functor" $\Gamma(\mathfrak{F})(= \Gamma(X, \mathfrak{F}) = \mathfrak{F}(X))$ is left exact: if $0 \to \mathfrak{F} \to \mathfrak{G} \to \mathfrak{H}$ is exact, then $0 \to \Gamma(\mathfrak{F}) \to \Gamma(\mathfrak{G}) \to \Gamma(\mathfrak{H})$ is exact.

This follows from (iii) above.

(vii) Direct sum. Let $(\mathfrak{F}_i)_{i \in I}$ be any family of $\mathfrak{O}$-Modules. Their direct sum $\mathfrak{F} = \bigoplus_{i \in I} \mathfrak{F}_i$ is the sheaf $U \mapsto \bigoplus_{i \in I} \mathfrak{F}_i(U)$. If each $\mathfrak{F}_i$ is equal to $\mathfrak{O}$, we write $\mathfrak{O}^{(I)}$ for the direct sum. In particular, if I is finite and has n elements, we write $\mathfrak{O}^n$ for the direct sum of n copies of $\mathfrak{O}$.

(viii) Tensor product. If $\mathfrak{F}$, $\mathfrak{G}$ are $\mathfrak{O}$-Modules, their tensor product $\mathfrak{F} \otimes_{\mathfrak{O}} \mathfrak{G}$ is defined to be the sheaf associated with the presheaf $U \mapsto \mathfrak{F}(U) \otimes_{\mathfrak{O}(U)} \mathfrak{G}(U)$. Since $\otimes$ commutes with $\varinjlim$, we have $(\mathfrak{F} \otimes_{\mathfrak{O}} \mathfrak{G})_x \cong \mathfrak{F}_x \otimes_{\mathfrak{O}_x} \mathfrak{G}_x$. This tensor product has all the usual properties: it is commutative, associative, distributive over $\bigoplus$, and is right exact in each variable (look at the stalks and use (7.1)). Also $\mathfrak{F} \otimes_{\mathfrak{O}} \mathfrak{O} \cong \mathfrak{F}$.

(ix) Global Hom. $\mathrm{Hom}_{\mathfrak{O}}(\mathfrak{F}, \mathfrak{G})$ is the group of all $\mathfrak{O}$-Module homomorphisms $\varphi : \mathfrak{F} \to \mathfrak{G}$. It has a natural $\mathfrak{O}(X)$-module structure: if $\varphi : \mathfrak{F} \to \mathfrak{G}$ and $s \in \mathfrak{O}(X)$, define $s\varphi : \mathfrak{F} \to \mathfrak{G}$ by $(s\varphi)(U) = s|U \,.\, \varphi(U)$.

(x) Sheaf $\mathcal{H}om$. The presheaf $U \mapsto \mathrm{Hom}_{\mathfrak{O}|U}$ is easily checked to be a <u>sheaf</u>, denoted by $\mathcal{H}om_{\mathcal{O}}(\mathfrak{F}, \mathcal{G})$. Thus $\Gamma(X, \mathcal{H}om_{\mathcal{O}}(\mathfrak{F}, \mathcal{G})) = \mathrm{Hom}_{\mathcal{O}}(\mathfrak{F}, \mathcal{G})$. $\mathcal{H}om_{\mathcal{O}}(\mathfrak{F}, \mathcal{G})$ has a natural $\mathcal{O}$-Module structure. Both Hom and $\mathcal{H}om$ are left exact in each variable (contravariant in the 1st variable, covariant in the 2nd). We have $\mathcal{H}om_{\mathcal{O}}(\mathcal{O}, \mathcal{G}) \cong \mathcal{G}$.

Let $f_x \in (\mathcal{H}om_{\mathcal{O}}(\mathfrak{F}, \mathcal{G}))_x$. Then f_x is represented by say $f : \mathfrak{F} \mid U \to \mathcal{G} \mid U$, which gives rise to a homomorphism $\mathfrak{F}_x \to \mathcal{G}_x$, i.e. an element of $\mathrm{Hom}_{\mathcal{O}_x}(\mathfrak{F}_x, \mathcal{G}_x)$. Hence we have $\mathcal{O}_x$-module homomorphism

$$(\mathcal{H}om_{\mathcal{O}}(\mathfrak{F}, \mathcal{G}))_x \to \mathrm{Hom}_{\mathcal{O}_x}(\mathfrak{F}_x, \mathcal{G}_x)$$

<u>which in general is neither injective nor surjective</u> (but see (7.9)).

(xi) <u>Direct image</u>. Let $\Psi = (\psi, \theta) : (X, \mathcal{O}_X) \to (Y, \mathcal{O}_Y)$ be a morphism of ringed spaces. If $\mathfrak{F}$ is an $\mathcal{O}_X$-Module (thus a sheaf on X), we define its <u>direct image</u> $\Psi_* \mathfrak{F}$, which is an $\mathcal{O}_Y$-Module (thus a sheaf on Y) as follows: $\Psi_* \mathfrak{F}(V) = \mathfrak{F}(\psi^{-1}(V))$ for each open set V in Y; $\mathfrak{F}(\psi^{-1}(V))$ is an $\mathcal{O}_X(\psi^{-1}(V))$-module, hence an $\mathcal{O}_Y(V)$-module via the homomorphism $\theta(V) : \mathcal{O}_Y(V) \to \mathcal{O}_X(\psi^{-1}(V))$.

Ψ_* is a left-exact functor from $\mathcal{O}_X$-Modules to $\mathcal{O}_Y$-Modules. For the section functor Γ is left exact by (7.2).

Hence if $0 \to \mathfrak{F}' \to \mathfrak{F} \to \mathfrak{F}''$ is an exact sequence of $\mathfrak{O}_X$-Modules, then $\mathfrak{O} \to \Gamma(\psi^{-1}(V), \mathfrak{F}') \to \Gamma(\psi^{-1}(V), \mathfrak{F}) \to \Gamma(\psi^{-1}(V), \mathfrak{F}'')$ is exact for each open $V \subseteq Y$; hence $0 \to \Psi_*\mathfrak{F}' \to \Psi_*\mathfrak{F} \to \Psi_*\mathfrak{F}''$ is exact.

In particular, if Y is the ringed space consisting of a single point and the ring $\mathfrak{O}(X)$, then $\Psi_*(\mathfrak{F}) = \mathfrak{F}(X) = \Gamma(X, \mathfrak{F})$. Thus $\Psi_*(\mathfrak{F}) = \mathfrak{F}(X) = \Gamma(X, \mathfrak{F})$. Thus Ψ_* is a 'relativization' of the section functor Γ.

QUASI-COHERENT AND COHERENT SHEAVES

If $\mathfrak{F}$ is an $\mathfrak{O}$-Module, a homomorphism $u : \mathfrak{O} \to \mathfrak{F}$ gives rise to $s = u(X)(1) \in \mathfrak{F}(X)$, i.e. to a global section of $\mathfrak{F}$. Conversely, given $s \in \mathfrak{F}(X)$ we may reconstruct u: if U is open in X and $t \in \mathfrak{O}(U)$, then $u(t) = t \, . \, (s \mid U)$. Hence we have a one-one correspondence between $\mathfrak{O}$-Module homomorphisms $\mathfrak{O} \to \mathfrak{F}$ and global sections of $\mathfrak{F}$, hence between $\mathfrak{O}$-Module homomorphisms $u : \mathfrak{O}^{(I)} \to \mathfrak{F}$ and families $(s_i)_{i \in I}$ of global sections of $\mathfrak{F}$, where I is any index set. u is an epimorphism if and only if each $\mathfrak{F}_x$ is generated (as an $\mathfrak{O}_x$-module) by the $(s_i)_x$ (for u is an epimorphism if and only if each $u_x : (\mathfrak{O}_x)^{(I)} \to \mathfrak{F}_x$ is an epimorphism, by (7.1)).

$\mathfrak{F}$ is said to be quasi-coherent if each $x \in X$ has an open neighbourhood U such that $\mathfrak{F} \mid U$ is the cokernel of a homomorphism $\mathcal{O}^{(I)} \mid U \to \mathcal{O}^{(J)} \mid U$, where the index sets I, J are of arbitrary cardinal (and depend on U). Clearly $\mathcal{O}$ itself is quasi-coherent as an $\mathcal{O}$-Module.

Thus $\mathfrak{F}$ is quasi-coherent if and only if $\mathfrak{F}$ is locally generated by its sections and if the 'sheaf of relations' is locally generated by its sections.

An $\mathcal{O}$-module $\mathfrak{F}$ is of finite type if each $x \in X$ has an open neighbourhood U such that $\mathfrak{F} \mid U$ is generated by a finite set of sections of $\mathfrak{F}$ over U, i.e. if there exists an epimorphism $\mathcal{O}^p \mid U \to \mathfrak{F} \mid U$ for some integer $p > 0$. If $\mathfrak{F}$, $\mathfrak{G}$ are of finite type, then so are $\mathfrak{F} \oplus \mathfrak{G}$ and $\mathfrak{F} \otimes_{\mathcal{O}} \mathfrak{G}$ (the latter because $\otimes$ is right exact). If $\mathfrak{F}$ is of finite type and $\mathfrak{G}$ is a homomorphic image of $\mathfrak{F}$, then $\mathfrak{G}$ is of finite type.

$\mathfrak{F}$ is said to be coherent if

(i) $\mathfrak{F}$ is of finite type;

(ii) for each open set U in X and each homomorphism $\varphi : \mathcal{O}^n \mid U \to \mathfrak{F} \mid U$ (n a positive integer), $\mathrm{Ker}(\varphi)$ is of finite type.

Clearly a coherent sheaf is quasi-coherent. All these

properties (quasi-coherence, finite type, coherence) are <u>local</u> with respect to the base-space X.

We shall use the following notation. If U is an open set in X, the phrase '$f : \mathfrak{F} \to \mathfrak{G}$ (over U)' shall mean $f : \mathfrak{F} \mid U \to \mathfrak{G} \mid U$. Similarly for diagrams of sheaves and homomorphisms.

Lemma (7.3). If $\mathfrak{F}$ is a subsheaf of $\mathfrak{G}$, and $\mathfrak{F}$ is of finite type and $\mathfrak{G}$ is coherent, then $\mathfrak{F}$ is coherent.

<u>Proof</u>. Let $i : \mathfrak{F} \to \mathfrak{G}$ be the embedding. If we have $f : \mathfrak{O}^n \to \mathfrak{F}$ (over U), then $i \circ f : \mathfrak{O}^n \to \mathfrak{G}$ (over U); but $\mathfrak{G}$ is coherent, hence $\ker f = \ker i \circ f$ is of finite type.

Lemma (7.4). Let $\mathfrak{G}$, $\mathfrak{H}$ be $\mathfrak{O}$-Modules. If we have a diagram

$$\begin{array}{ccccc} \mathfrak{G} & \xrightarrow{h} & \mathfrak{H} & \longrightarrow & 0 \\ & & \uparrow{\scriptstyle f} & & \\ & & \mathfrak{O}^p & & \end{array} \qquad \text{(over a neighbourhood of } x \in X)$$

with the row exact, then there exists an $\mathfrak{O}$-Module homomorphism $g : \mathfrak{O}^p \to \mathfrak{G}$ (over a (smaller) neighbourhood of x), such that $h \circ g = f$.

<u>Proof</u>. The map f defines p sections $s_i (1 \leqslant i \leqslant p)$ belonging to $\mathfrak{H}(U)$ (U some open neighbourhood of x). Explicitly,

$f(U)$ maps $\mathcal{O}(U)^p$ into $\mathcal{H}(U)$, and s_i is the image of the ith generator e_i of $\mathcal{O}(U)^p$. Since h is an epimorphism, there exist $g_{i,x} \in \mathcal{G}_x$ such that $h_x(g_{i,x}) = (s_i)_x$ $(1 \leqslant i \leqslant p)$. Each $g_{i,x}$ is represented by say $g_i' \in \mathcal{H}(U_i)$; $h(g_i')$ agrees with s_i at x, hence in some open neighbourhood of x, say V_i $(\subseteq U_i \cap U)$. Let $V = V_1 \cap \ldots \cap V_p$, then the $g_i = g_i' \mid V$ define $g : \mathcal{O}^p \to \mathcal{G}$ (over V), and we have (over V) $h \circ g(e_i) = h(g_i)$ $= s_i \mid V = f(e_i)$, hence $h \circ g = f$.

Theorem (7.5). If $0 \to \mathcal{F} \xrightarrow{f} \mathcal{G} \xrightarrow{g} \mathcal{H} \to 0$ is an exact sequence of $\mathcal{O}$-Modules on X, and if any two of $\mathcal{F}$, $\mathcal{G}$, $\mathcal{H}$ are coherent, then so is the third.

Proof. (1) $\mathcal{G}$, $\mathcal{H}$ coherent. By (7.3) it is enough to show that $\mathcal{F}$ is of finite type. Let $x \in X$. Since $\mathcal{G}$ is of finite type we have an epimorphism $u : \mathcal{O}^p \to \mathcal{G}$ (over some neighbourhood of x). Since $\mathcal{H}$ is coherent, the kernel of $g \circ u$ is of finite type, hence we have an exact sequence

$$\mathcal{O}^q \xrightarrow{v} \mathcal{O}^p \xrightarrow{gu} \mathcal{H} \to 0 \text{ (over some neighbourhood U of x).}$$

Hence a commutative diagram with exact rows:

$$\begin{array}{ccccccccc} & & \mathcal{O}^q & \xrightarrow{v} & \mathcal{O}^p & \xrightarrow{gu} & \mathcal{H} & \to & 0 \\ & & \downarrow w & & \downarrow u & & \downarrow id & & \\ 0 & \to & \mathcal{F} & \xrightarrow[f]{} & \mathcal{G} & \xrightarrow[g]{} & \mathcal{H} & \to & 0 \end{array} \quad \text{(over U).}$$

We wish to define $w : \mathcal{O}^q \to \mathfrak{F}$ such that $fw = uv$, and show that w is an epimorphism (over U). Since $guv = 0$, $\mathrm{Im}(uv) \subseteq \mathrm{Ker}(g) = \mathrm{Im}(f)$, so we can define w to be $f^{-1}uv$. To show that w is an epimorphism, let $y \in U$, consider the corresponding diagram of stalks over y, and verify that w_y is an epimorphism by diagram-chasing. Hence by (7.1) w is an epimorphism and therefore $\mathfrak{F}$ is of finite type.

(2) <u>$\mathfrak{F}$, $\mathfrak{G}$ coherent.</u> $\mathfrak{G}$ is of finite type, hence so is $\mathfrak{H}$. Let $x \in X$ and let $u : \mathcal{O}^p \to \mathfrak{H}$ be a homomorphism (over an open neighbourhood of x). By (7.4) we can lift u to $v : \mathcal{O}^p \to \mathfrak{G}$ (over a smaller open neighbourhood of x), so that $gv = u$. $\mathfrak{F}$ is of finite type, hence we have say $e : \mathcal{O}^q \to \mathfrak{F}$ (over some open neighbourhood of x). Hence we have the following diagram:

$$\begin{array}{ccccccccc}
0 & \longrightarrow & \mathfrak{F} & \xrightarrow{f} & \mathfrak{G} & \xrightarrow{g} & \mathfrak{H} & \longrightarrow & 0 \\
 & & {\scriptstyle e}\uparrow & & {\scriptstyle t}\uparrow & & \uparrow{\scriptstyle u} & & \\
0 & \longrightarrow & \mathcal{O}^q & \underset{r}{\overset{h}{\rightleftarrows}} & \mathcal{O}^{p+q} & \underset{s}{\overset{k}{\rightleftarrows}} & \mathcal{O}^p & \longrightarrow & 0
\end{array}$$

(over a neighbourhood of x)

in which the rows are exact and the bottom row is split: $rh = 1$, $ks = 1$, $hr + sk = 1$. Define $t = fer + vk : \mathcal{O}^{p+q} \to \mathfrak{G}$, then the diagram is commutative. Since $\mathfrak{G}$ is coherent, the kernel of t is of finite type and we can therefore enlarge the diagram:

$$
\begin{array}{ccccccccc}
0 & \longrightarrow & \mathfrak{F} & \xrightarrow{f} & \mathfrak{G} & \xrightarrow{g} & \mathfrak{H} & \longrightarrow & 0 \\
 & & e\uparrow & & t\uparrow & & \uparrow u & & \\
0 & \longrightarrow & \mathfrak{O}^q & \xrightarrow[h]{} & \mathfrak{O}^{p+q} & \xrightarrow[k]{} & \mathfrak{O}^p & \longrightarrow & 0 \\
 & & & & w\uparrow & & \uparrow kw & & \\
 & & & & \mathfrak{O}^n & \xrightarrow[id]{} & \mathfrak{O}^n & &
\end{array}
$$

(over a neighbourhood of x)

Verify that the right-hand column is exact, e.g. by considering the corresponding diagram of stalks over a point $y \in U$. Hence $\mathfrak{H}$ is coherent.

(3) <u>$\mathfrak{F}$, $\mathfrak{H}$ coherent</u>. Since $\mathfrak{F}$ and $\mathfrak{H}$ are of finite type we have

$$
\begin{array}{ccccccccc}
0 & \longrightarrow & \mathfrak{F} & \xrightarrow{f} & \mathfrak{G} & \xrightarrow{g} & \mathfrak{H} & \longrightarrow & 0 \\
 & & u\uparrow & & v\,\vdots\!\uparrow & & \uparrow w & & \\
0 & \longrightarrow & \mathfrak{O}^q & \longrightarrow & \mathfrak{O}^{p+q} & \longrightarrow & \mathfrak{O}^p & \longrightarrow & 0
\end{array}
$$

(over some open neighbourhood of x)

with u, w epimorphisms; hence as in (2) we can define $v : \mathfrak{O}^{p+q} \to \mathfrak{G}$. Since u, w are epi, so is v (by the 5 lemma). Hence $\mathfrak{G}$ is of finite type.

Now let $u : \mathfrak{O}^r \to \mathfrak{G}$ be a homomorphism (over some open neighbourhood of x); we have to show that Ker(u) is of finite type. Since $\mathfrak{H}$ is coherent we have an exact sequence of the form $\mathfrak{O}^s \xrightarrow{v} \mathfrak{O}^r \xrightarrow{gu} \mathfrak{H}$ (over some open neighbourhood u of x), hence a diagram

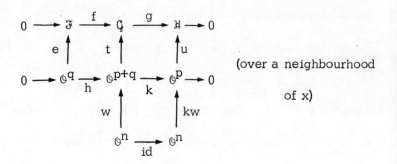

$$\begin{array}{ccccccccc}
0 & \longrightarrow & \mathfrak{F} & \xrightarrow{f} & \mathfrak{G} & \xrightarrow{g} & \mathfrak{H} & \longrightarrow & 0 \\
 & & {\scriptstyle w}\uparrow & & \uparrow{\scriptstyle u} & & \uparrow{\scriptstyle id} & & \\
 & & \mathfrak{O}^s & \xrightarrow[v]{} & \mathfrak{O}^r & \xrightarrow[gu]{} & \mathfrak{H} & &
\end{array} \qquad \text{(over } U\text{);}$$

here we have $guv = 0$, hence $\mathrm{Im}(uv) \subseteq \mathrm{Ker}(g) = \mathrm{Im}(f)$, so we can define $w : \mathfrak{O}^s \to \mathfrak{F}$ (over U) so that $uv = fw$. Now $\mathfrak{F}$ is coherent, hence the kernel of w is of finite type, hence we can enlarge the diagram:

$$\begin{array}{ccccccccc}
0 & \longrightarrow & \mathfrak{F} & \xrightarrow{f} & \mathfrak{G} & \xrightarrow{g} & \mathfrak{H} & \longrightarrow & 0 \\
 & & {\scriptstyle w}\uparrow & & \uparrow{\scriptstyle u} & & \uparrow{\scriptstyle id} & & \\
 & & \mathfrak{O}^s & \xrightarrow{v} & \mathfrak{O}^r & \xrightarrow{gu} & \mathfrak{H} & & \\
 & & {\scriptstyle p}\uparrow & & \uparrow{\scriptstyle vp} & & & & \\
 & & \mathfrak{O}^t & \xrightarrow[id]{} & \mathfrak{O}^t & & & &
\end{array} \qquad \text{(over some open neighbourhood of } x\text{).}$$

Here the first column (as well as the top row) is exact, and we verify (e.g. by diagram-chasing in the stalks) that the second column is exact. Hence Ker(u) is of finite type and therefore $\mathfrak{G}$ is coherent.

Corollary (7.6). $\mathfrak{F}$ and $\mathfrak{G}$ are coherent if and only if $\mathfrak{F} \oplus \mathfrak{G}$ is coherent.

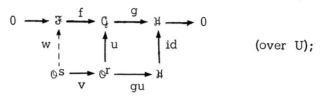

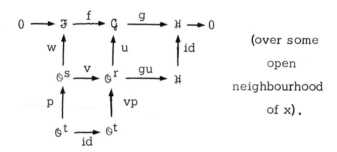

Proof. If $\mathfrak{F}$, $\mathfrak{G}$ are coherent, the exact sequence $0 \to \mathfrak{F} \to \mathfrak{F} \oplus \mathfrak{G} \to \mathfrak{G} \to 0$ shows that $\mathfrak{F} \oplus \mathfrak{G}$ is coherent. If $\mathfrak{F} \oplus \mathfrak{G}$ is coherent then $\mathfrak{F}$ is of finite type because it is a homomorphic image of $\mathfrak{F} \oplus \mathfrak{G}$; it is also a subsheaf of $\mathfrak{F} \oplus \mathfrak{G}$, hence coherent by (7.3).

Corollary (7.7). If $\varphi : \mathfrak{F} \to \mathfrak{G}$ is a homomorphism of coherent $\mathfrak{O}$-Modules, then the kernel, image and cokernel of φ are all coherent.

Proof. $\mathrm{Im}(\varphi)$ is a homomorphic image of $\mathfrak{F}$, hence is of finite type; it is also a sub-Module of $\mathfrak{G}$, hence coherent by (7.3). Now apply (7.5) to the exact sequences

$$0 \to \mathrm{Ker}(\varphi) \to \mathfrak{F} \to \mathrm{Im}(\varphi) \to 0$$

$$0 \to \mathrm{Im}(\varphi) \to \mathfrak{G} \to \mathrm{Coker}(\varphi) \to 0.$$

Corollary (7.8). If $\mathfrak{F}_1 \xrightarrow{\varphi} \mathfrak{F}_2 \to \mathfrak{F}_3 \to \mathfrak{F}_4 \xrightarrow{\psi} \mathfrak{F}_5$ is an exact sequence in which all but $\mathfrak{F}_3$ are coherent, then $\mathfrak{F}_3$ is coherent.

Proof. From (7.7) and the exact sequence $0 \to \mathrm{Coker}(\varphi) \to \mathfrak{F}_3 \to \mathrm{Ker}(\psi) \to 0$.

Proposition (7.9). If $\mathfrak{F}$, $\mathfrak{G}$ are coherent $\mathfrak{O}$-Modules, then $\mathfrak{F} \otimes_{\mathfrak{O}} \mathfrak{G}$ and $\mathcal{H}om_{\mathfrak{O}}(\mathfrak{F}, \mathfrak{G})$ are coherent.

Proof. Consider $\mathfrak{F} \underset{\mathfrak{O}}{\otimes} \mathfrak{G}$. Let $x \in X$; since $\mathfrak{F}$ is coherent there is an exact sequence.

$$(*) \qquad \mathcal{O}^q \to \mathcal{O}^p \to \mathcal{F} \to 0 \quad \text{(over some open neighbourhood U of x);}$$

hence, as tensoring with $\mathcal{G}$ is right exact and $\mathcal{O} \otimes \mathcal{G} \cong \mathcal{G}$, an exact sequence

$$\mathcal{G}^q \to \mathcal{G}^p \to \mathcal{F} \otimes \mathcal{G} \to 0 \quad \text{(over U);}$$

since $\mathcal{G}$ is coherent, so are $\mathcal{G}^p$, $\mathcal{G}^q$ by (7.6), hence $\mathcal{F} \otimes \mathcal{G}$ is coherent by (7.7) and the fact that coherence is a <u>local</u> property.

For $\mathcal{H}om_{\mathcal{O}}(\mathcal{F}, \mathcal{G})$, operate on (*) with $\mathcal{H}om_{\mathcal{O}}(\ \ , \mathcal{G})$. The argument is similar.

Proposition (7.10). If $\mathcal{F}$, $\mathcal{G}$ are $\mathcal{O}$-Modules and $\mathcal{F}$ is coherent, the mapping.

$$(\mathcal{H}om_{\mathcal{O}}(\mathcal{F}, \mathcal{G}))_x \to \mathrm{Hom}_{\mathcal{O}_x}(\mathcal{F}_x, \mathcal{G}_x)$$

is an isomorphism.

<u>Proof</u>. From (*) we have $\mathcal{O}_x^q \to \mathcal{O}_x^p \to \mathcal{F}_x \to 0$ exact, hence by the left exactness of $\mathcal{H}om_{\mathcal{O}}$ and $\mathrm{Hom}_{\mathcal{O}_x}$ we have exact sequences

$$\begin{array}{ccccccc} 0 \to & (\mathcal{H}om_{\mathcal{O}}(\mathcal{F}, \mathcal{G}))_x & \to & (\mathcal{H}om_{\mathcal{O}}(\mathcal{O}^p, \mathcal{G}))_x & \to & (\mathcal{H}om_{\mathcal{O}}(\mathcal{O}^q, \mathcal{G}))_x \\ & \downarrow & & \downarrow & & \downarrow \\ 0 \to & \mathrm{Hom}_{\mathcal{O}_x}(\mathcal{F}_x, \mathcal{G}_x) & \to & \mathrm{Hom}_{\mathcal{O}_x}(\mathcal{O}_x^p, \mathcal{G}_x) & \to & \mathrm{Hom}_{\mathcal{O}_x}(\mathcal{O}_x^q, \mathcal{G}_x). \end{array}$$

Since $\mathcal{H}om_{\mathcal{O}}(\mathcal{O}^p, \mathcal{G}) = \mathcal{G}^p$, the second and third vertical arrows are isomorphisms, hence so is the first.

If $\mathfrak{O}$ itself is coherent as an $\mathfrak{O}$-Module, we shall say that $\mathfrak{O}$ is a <u>coherent sheaf of rings</u>.

Proposition (7.11). Let $\mathfrak{O}$ be a coherent sheaf of rings and let $\mathfrak{F}$ be an $\mathfrak{O}$-Module. Then $\mathfrak{F}$ is coherent if and only if it is locally finitely presented, i.e. for each $x \in X$ there is an exact sequence $\mathfrak{O}^q \to \mathfrak{O}^p \to \mathfrak{F} \to 0$ over some neighbourhood of x.

Proof. If $\mathfrak{F}$ is coherent it is locally finitely presented (whether $\mathfrak{O}$ is coherent or not). Conversely, if $\mathfrak{O}$ is coherent, so are $\mathfrak{O}^p$ and $\mathfrak{O}^q$ by (7.6), hence so is $\mathfrak{F}$ by (7.7) (since coherence is a local property).

Chapter 8

SHEAF COHOMOLOGY

We need some basic homological algebra. Let $\underline{C}$ be an abelian category (for our purposes, $\underline{C}$ will be the category of $\mathcal{O}$-Modules, where $\mathcal{O}$ is a sheaf of rings on a topological space X). An object I in $\underline{C}$ is injective if the functor $A \mapsto I(A) = \mathrm{Hom}(A, I)$ is exact and not merely left exact: that is to say, whenever $A \to B$ is a monomorphism in $\underline{C}$, the map $I(B) \to (IA)$ is surjective.

The category $\underline{C}$ has enough injectives if every object in $\underline{C}$ can be embedded in an injective object. Suppose that $\underline{C}$ has enough injectives, and let A be an object in $\underline{C}$. Then there exists an injective I^0 in $\underline{C}$ and a monomorphism $\mu : A \to I^0$. Let $A^1 = \mathrm{Coker}(\mu)$, then there exists an injective I^1 in $\underline{C}$ and a monomorphism $\mu^1 : A^1 \to I^1$. Let $A^2 = \mathrm{Coker}(\mu^1)$, and so on. The short exact sequences $0 \to A \to I^0 \to A^1 \to 0$, $0 \to A^1 \to I^1 \to A^2 \to 0$, etc., then stick together to form a long exact sequence:

(*) $$0 \to A \to I^0 \xrightarrow{a^0} I^1 \xrightarrow{a^1} I^2 \xrightarrow{a^2} \cdots$$

called an <u>injective resolution</u> of A.

Now let F be a covariant additive left exact functor on $\underline{C}$ with values in an abelian category $\underline{C}'$. If we operate on (*) with F, we get a complex, so we can form its cohomology:

$$H^p = \text{Ker } F(\alpha^p)/\text{Im } F(\alpha^{p-1}) \quad (p \geq 0;\ \alpha^{-1} = 0).$$

The central fact is that H^p depends (up to isomorphism) only on F and A and not on the injective resolution: it is denoted by $R^pF(A)$, and R^pF is an additive functor, called the pth <u>right derived functor</u> of F. Since F is left exact, we have $R^oF = F$.

If A is injective then $R^pF(A) = 0$ for all $p > 0$; for $0 \to A \to A \to 0$ is an injective resolution of A.

Theorem (8.1). If $0 \to A \xrightarrow{\alpha} B \xrightarrow{\beta} C \to 0$ is an exact sequence in $\underline{C}$, and if F is a covariant additive left exact functor on $\underline{C}$ with values in an abelian category $\underline{C}'$, then there is an exact sequence in $\underline{C}'$:

$$0 \longrightarrow F(A) \xrightarrow{F(\alpha)} F(B) \xrightarrow{F(\beta)} F(C)$$
$$\xrightarrow{\partial} R^1F(A) \xrightarrow{R^1F(\alpha)} R^1F(B) \xrightarrow{R^1F(\beta)} R^1F(C) \xrightarrow{\partial} R^2F(A) \to \ldots$$

For the definition of the 'coboundary morphisms' $\partial : R^{p-1}F(C) \to R^pF(A)$ and the proof of (8.1) we refer to Godement's book (or any book on homological algebra).

GROTHENDIECK COHOMOLOGY

We shall apply this machinery to the following situation: $(X, \mathfrak{O})$ is a ringed space and $\underline{C}$ is the category of $\mathfrak{O}$-Modules. Then $\underline{C}$ is abelian (as remarked in Chapter 7) and in fact $\underline{C}$ has enough injectives (proof e.g. in Godement's book). By (7.2), the section functor Γ is a left exact functor on $\underline{C}$ with values in the category of $\mathfrak{O}(X)$-modules. The <u>cohomology groups</u> (which are in fact $\mathfrak{O}(X)$-modules) <u>of</u> X <u>with coefficients in the</u> $\mathfrak{O}$-Module $\mathfrak{F}$ are then defined to be

$$H^p(X, \mathfrak{F}) = R^p\Gamma(\mathfrak{F}) \quad (p \geqslant 0).$$

In particular, $H^0(X, \mathfrak{F}) = \Gamma(X, \mathfrak{F})$. From (8.1) we have an exact cohomology sequence: if $0 \to \mathfrak{F} \to \mathfrak{G} \to \mathfrak{H} \to 0$ is an exact sequence of $\mathfrak{O}$-Modules, then the sequence

$$0 \to \Gamma(X,\mathfrak{F}) \to \Gamma(X, \mathfrak{G}) \to \Gamma(X, \mathfrak{H}) \to H^1(X, \mathfrak{F}) \to H^1(X, \mathfrak{G})$$
$$\to H^1(X, \mathfrak{H}) \to H^2(X, \mathfrak{F}) \to \dots$$

is exact.

This definition of the cohomology groups $H^p(X, \mathfrak{F})$ is due to Grothendieck.

ČECH COHOMOLOGY

There is an earlier definition of sheaf cohomology,

modelled on Čech theory, which goes as follows. Let $\mathfrak{U} = (U_i)_{i \in I}$ be any open covering of X. If $\sigma = (i_0, \ldots, i_p)$ is any p-simplex, i.e. sequence of p + 1 elements of the index set I, let U_σ denote the intersection $U_{i_0} \cap \ldots \cap U_{i_p}$. An (alternating) p-cochain of the covering $\mathfrak{U}$ with coefficients in the sheaf $\mathfrak{F}$ is a function c which associates with each p-simplex σ an element $c_\sigma \in \mathfrak{F}(U_\sigma)$ in such a way that c_σ is alternating in the indices $i_0, \ldots, i_p$, and $c_\sigma = 0$ whenever any two of the indices are equal. The p-cochains form a group $C^p(\mathfrak{U}, \mathfrak{F})$, which has a natural $\mathcal{O}(X)$-module structure: if $a \in \mathcal{O}(X)$, then $(ac)_\sigma$ is defined to be $(a \mid U_\sigma) . c_\sigma$. If we order the index set I linearly then we may write $C^p(U, \mathfrak{F}) = \prod_\sigma \mathfrak{F}(U_\sigma)$, where in the product σ runs over all p-simplexes $(i_0, \ldots, i_p)$ such that $i_0 < i_1 < \ldots < i_p$.

Define a coboundary homomorphism

$$d : C^p(\mathfrak{U}, \mathfrak{F}) \to C^{p+1}(\mathfrak{U}, \mathfrak{F})$$

as follows: if $c \in C^p(\mathfrak{U}, \mathfrak{F})$, then

$$(dc)_{i_0 \ldots i_{p+1}} = \sum_{k=0}^{p+1} (-1)^k c_{i_0 \ldots \hat{i}_k \ldots i_{p+1}} \mid U_{i_0 \ldots i_{p+1}}$$

One verifies that $d^2 = 0$. Thus $C^\bullet(\mathfrak{U}, \mathfrak{F}) = \bigoplus_{p \geq 0} C^p(\mathfrak{U}, \mathfrak{F})$ is a complex of $\mathcal{O}(X)$-modules, and we define the pth cohomology group of the covering $\mathfrak{U}$ with coefficients in $\mathfrak{F}$ to be

$$H^p(\mathfrak{U}, \mathfrak{F}) = H^p(C^\bullet(\mathfrak{U}, \mathfrak{F})) \quad (p > 0).$$

Next one shows that a refinement $\mathfrak{U}'$ of $\mathfrak{U}$ gives rise to well-defined homomorphisms $H^p(\mathfrak{U}, \mathfrak{F}) \to H^p(\mathfrak{U}', \mathfrak{F})$ with the usual transitivity properties; these enable us to define the Čech cohomology groups of X with coefficients in $\mathfrak{F}$:

$$\check{H}^p(X, \mathfrak{F}) = \varinjlim_{\mathfrak{U}} H^p(\mathfrak{U}, \mathfrak{F}),$$

the direct limit being taken over arbitrarily fine open coverings $\mathfrak{U}$ of X.

The advantage of Čech cohomology is that one stands some chance of being able to compute it in given situations. The disadvantage, which is a serious one, is that the cohomology sequence in Čech cohomology is not necessarily exact. It is always the case that $\check{H}^0 = H^0$ and $\check{H}^1 = H^1$ (so that the Čech cohomology sequence is always exact as far as $\check{H}^1$) but $\check{H}^p(X, \mathfrak{F})$ and $H^p(X, \mathfrak{F})$ are not necessarily the same for $p > 1$. There is a spectral sequence relating the two cohomologies (details in Godement's book), from which one can assert that $\check{H}^p = H^p$ for all p under suitable hypotheses on X or $\mathfrak{F}$ or both. Here are two such 'comparison theorems':

Theorem (8.2). Let $\mathfrak{U}$ be an open covering of X, let $\mathfrak{F}$ be a sheaf on X, and suppose that, for all simplexes $\sigma = (i_0, \ldots, i_p)$, we have $H^p(U_\sigma, \mathfrak{F} \mid U_\sigma) = 0$ for all $q > 0$. Then $H^q(X, \mathfrak{F}) = H^q(\mathfrak{U}, \mathfrak{F})$ for all $q \geqslant 0$.

Theorem (8.3). (Cartan). Let $\mathfrak{U}$ be an open covering of X and $\mathfrak{F}$ a sheaf on X such that

(i) $\mathfrak{U}$ is closed under finite intersections;

(ii) the sets of $\mathfrak{U}$ form a basis of X;

(iii) $\check{H}^q(U, \mathfrak{F} \mid U) = 0$ for all $U \in \mathfrak{U}$ and all $q > 0$.

Then $\check{H}^q(X, \mathfrak{F}) \cong H^q(X, \mathfrak{F})$ for all $q \geqslant 0$.

Theorems (8.2) and (8.3) are proved in Godement's book. We shall sketch a proof of (8.2) avoiding the use of spectral sequences, but not (8.3).

There are other comparison theorems: thus the conclusion of (8.3) is valid if X is paracompact (and Hausdorff) and $\mathfrak{F}$ is any sheaf of abelian groups. This one is of use if X is a differentiable manifold or a complex manifold, but not in algebraic geometry.

THE ČECH RESOLUTION OF A SHEAF

Let $(X, \mathcal{O})$ be a ringed space and $\mathfrak{F}$ an $\mathcal{O}$-Module, and let $\mathfrak{U} = (U_i)_{i \in I}$ be any open covering of X. For each open set V in X let $V \cap \mathfrak{U}$ denote the open covering $(V \cap U_i)_{i \in I}$ of V. Then we have $\mathcal{O}(V)$-modules $C^p(V \cap \mathfrak{U}, \mathfrak{F} \mid V)$ for each open set V in X and each integer $p \geq 0$, hence presheaves $V \mapsto C^p(V \cap \mathfrak{U}, \mathfrak{F} \mid V)$ for each $p \geq 0$. These presheaves are easily verified to be <u>sheaves</u>; denote them by $\mathcal{C}^p(\mathfrak{U}, \mathfrak{F})$. The coboundary operator $d : C^p \to C^{p+1}$ gives rise to sheaf homomorphisms

$$d : \mathcal{C}^p(\mathfrak{U}, \mathfrak{F}) \to \mathcal{C}^{p+1}(\mathfrak{U}, \mathfrak{F});$$

also we have a sheaf homomorphism $j : \mathfrak{F} \to \mathcal{C}^0(\mathfrak{U}, \mathfrak{F})$ defined as follows: if s is a section of $\mathfrak{F}$ over V, then

$$j(s) = (s \mid V \cap U_i)_{i \in I} \in C^0(V \cap \mathfrak{U}, \mathfrak{F} \mid V) = \mathcal{C}^0(\mathfrak{U}, \mathfrak{F})(V).$$

Proposition (8.4). The sequence

$$0 \to \mathfrak{F} \xrightarrow{j} \mathcal{C}^0(\mathfrak{U}, \mathfrak{F}) \xrightarrow{d^0} \mathcal{C}^1(\mathfrak{U}, \mathfrak{F}) \xrightarrow{d^1} \cdots$$

is exact.

<u>Proof</u>. (i) j is a monomorphism. For if $j(s) = 0$ then $s \mid V \cap V_i = 0$ for all $i \in I$, hence $s = 0$ (since the $V \cap U_i$ cover V).

(ii) $\mathrm{Im}(j) = \mathrm{Ker}(d^0)$. Let $s = (s_i) \in \mathcal{C}^0(V)$. If $ds = 0$ then

$(ds)_{ij} = 0$ for all pairs (i, j) in I, i.e. $s_i = s_j$ in $V \cap U_i \cap U_j$; hence the s_i fit together to give a section $\bar{s}$ of $\mathfrak{F}$ over V such that $\bar{s} \mid V \cap U_i = s_i$ for each i; i.e. $s = j(\bar{s})$. Conversely, if $s = j(\bar{s})$ for some $\bar{s} \in \mathfrak{F}(V)$, then $s_i = \bar{s} \mid V \cap U_i$, hence $(ds)_{ij} = s_j \mid V \cap U_i \cap U_j - s_i \mid V \cap U_i \cap U_j = 0$.

(iii) $\mathrm{Im}(d^{p-1}) = \mathrm{Ker}(d^p)$. We have $d^p \circ d^{p-1} = 0$, hence $\mathrm{Im}(d^{p-1}) \subseteq \mathrm{Ker}(d^p)$. Conversely, let $u \in (\mathcal{C}^p(\mathfrak{U}, \mathfrak{F}))_x$ be such that $du = 0$; say $x \in U_i$. Then there exists an open neighbourhood V of x contained in U_i and an element $s \in \mathcal{C}^p(\mathfrak{U}, \mathfrak{F})(V)$ such that $s_x = u$. If $\sigma = (i_0, \ldots, i_{p-1})$ is a $(p - 1)$-simplex, let $i\sigma$ denote the p-simplex $(i, i_0, \ldots, i_{p-1})$. We have $\mathcal{C}^p(\mathfrak{U}, \mathfrak{F})(V) = C^p(V \cap \mathfrak{U}, \mathfrak{F} \mid V)$, hence s is a family (s_τ) where τ runs through the p-simplexes and $s_\tau \in \mathfrak{F}(V \cap U_\tau)$. Define $t \in \mathcal{C}^{p-1}(\mathfrak{U}, \mathfrak{F})(V)$ by the rule $t_\sigma = s_{i\sigma} \in \mathfrak{F}(V \cap U_i \cap U_\sigma)$ $= \mathfrak{F}(V \cap U_\sigma)$; then

$$(dt)_\tau = \sum_{k=0}^{p} (-1)^k t_{\tau_k} \mid V \cap U_\tau \quad (\tau_k = \text{kth 'face' of } \tau)$$

$$= \sum_k (-1)^k s_{i\tau_k} \mid V \cap U_\tau$$

$$= s_\tau - (ds)_{i\tau}$$

$$= s_\tau \text{ since } ds = 0.$$

Hence $dt = s$ and therefore $\mathrm{Ker}(d^p) \subseteq \mathrm{Im}(d^{p-1})$.

Proof of (8.2). (i) Any product of injectives is injective (this is true in any abelian category).

(ii) If $\mathcal{I}$ is an injective $\mathcal{O}$-Module and U is open in X, then $\mathcal{I} \mid U$ is an injective $\mathcal{O} \mid U$-Module. For we have

$\mathrm{Hom}_{\mathcal{O} \mid U}(\mathcal{G}, \mathcal{I} \mid U) = \mathrm{Hom}_{\mathcal{O}}(\mathcal{G}^X, \mathcal{I})$ for any $\mathcal{O} \mid U$-Module $\mathcal{G}$, where $\mathcal{G}^X$ denotes the sheaf on X obtained by extending by zero outside U.

(iii) If $\mathcal{J}$ is an injective $\mathcal{O} \mid U$-Module and $i : U \to X$ is the embedding of the open set U in X, then $i_*\mathcal{J}$ is an injective $\mathcal{O}$-Module. For we have $\mathrm{Hom}_{\mathcal{O}}(\mathcal{F}, i_*\mathcal{J}) \cong \mathrm{Hom}_{\mathcal{O} \mid U}(\mathcal{F} \mid U, \mathcal{J})$ for any $\mathcal{O}$-Module $\mathcal{F}$.

(iv) With the notation of (8.4), we have $C^q(\mathfrak{U}, \mathcal{F})(V) = \prod_\sigma \mathcal{F}(V \cap U_\sigma) = \prod_\sigma i_{\sigma *}(\mathcal{F} \mid U_\sigma)(V)$ where σ runs through all q-simplexes $(i_0, \ldots, i_q)$ such that $i_0 < \ldots < i_q$ (with respect to some linear ordering of the index set I) and i_σ is the embedding of U_σ in X. Hence if $\mathcal{F}$ is injective, then $C^q(\mathfrak{U}, \mathcal{F})$ is injective by (i), (ii) and (iii).

(v) Let $0 \to \mathcal{F} \to \mathcal{I}^0 \to \mathcal{I}^1 \to \ldots$ be an injective resolution of $\mathcal{F}$. Then for each simplex σ the sequence $0 \to \mathcal{F} \mid U_\sigma \to \mathcal{I}^0 \mid U_\sigma \to \mathcal{I}^1 \mid U_\sigma \to \ldots$ is an injective resolution of $\mathcal{F} \mid U_\sigma$, by (iii) and the fact that restriction to an open set preserves exactness.

Hence this sequence can be used to calculate the cohomology of $\mathcal{F} \mid U_\sigma$. But by hypothesis $H^q(U_\sigma, \mathcal{F} \mid U_\sigma) = 0$ for all $q > 0$. Hence the sequence

$$0 \to \mathcal{F}(U_\sigma) \to \mathcal{I}^0(U_\sigma) \to \mathcal{I}^1(U_\sigma) \to \cdots$$

is exact. Hence, taking the product of these exact sequences for all q-simplexes σ, the sequence

$$0 \to C^q(\mathfrak{U}, \mathcal{F}) \to C^q(\mathfrak{U}, \mathcal{I}^0) \to C^q(\mathfrak{U}, \mathcal{I}^1) \to \cdots$$

is exact.

(vi) Consider next the Čech resolution of $\mathcal{I}^p$:

$$0 \to \mathcal{I}^p \to \mathcal{C}^0(\mathfrak{U}, \mathcal{I}^p) \to \mathcal{C}^1(\mathfrak{U}, \mathcal{I}^p) \to \cdots.$$

By (8.4) this is an exact sequence. By (iv) above, each $\mathcal{C}^q(\mathfrak{U}, \mathcal{I}^p)$ is injective, hence this is an injective resolution of $\mathcal{I}^p$; but $\mathcal{I}^p$ has zero cohomology in dimensions > 0, hence the sequence

$$0 \to \mathcal{I}^p(X) \to \mathcal{C}^0(\mathfrak{U}, \mathcal{I}^p)(X) \to \mathcal{C}^1(\mathfrak{U}, \mathcal{I}^p)(X) \to \cdots,$$

that is to say the sequence

$$0 \to \mathcal{I}^p(X) \to C^0(\mathfrak{U}, \mathcal{I}^p) \to C^1(\mathfrak{U}, \mathcal{I}^p) \to \cdots,$$

is exact.

(vii) We now have a double complex, in which all rows except for the top one, and all columns except for the left-hand one, are exact sequences (by (v) and (vi)):

$$
\begin{array}{ccccccccc}
 & & 0 & & 0 & & 0 & & \\
 & & \downarrow & & \downarrow & & \downarrow & & \\
0 & \to & \mathfrak{F}(X) & \to & C^0(\mathfrak{U}, \mathfrak{F}) & \to & C^1(\mathfrak{U}, \mathfrak{F}) & \to & \cdots \\
 & & \downarrow & & \downarrow & & \downarrow & & \\
0 & \to & \mathcal{J}^0(X) & \to & C^0(\mathfrak{U}, \mathcal{J}^0) & \to & C^1(\mathfrak{U}, \mathcal{J}^0) & \to & \cdots \\
 & & \downarrow & & \downarrow & & \downarrow & & \\
0 & \to & \mathcal{J}^1(X) & \to & C^0(\mathfrak{U}, \mathcal{J}^1) & \to & C^1(\mathfrak{U}, \mathcal{J}^1) & \to & \cdots \\
 & & \downarrow & & \downarrow & & \downarrow & & \\
 & & \vdots & & \vdots & & \vdots & &
\end{array}
$$

In such a situation the cohomology of the top row is isomorphic to the cohomology of the left-hand column. But in the present case the cohomology of the top row is the Čech cohomology $H^p(\mathfrak{U}, \mathfrak{F})$, and the cohomology of the left-hand column is Grothendieck cohomology $H^p(X, \mathfrak{F})$.

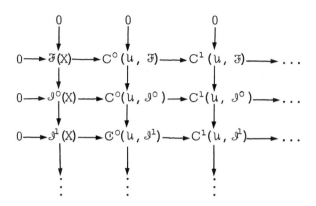

Chapter 9

COHOMOLOGY OF AFFINE SCHEMES

Let A be any commutative ring with identity element, and let X = Spec(A). We recall that, for any $f \in A$, the 'basic open set' D(f) is the set of all $x \in X$ such that $f(x) \neq 0$, i.e. such that $f \notin \mathfrak{j}_x$. Let M be any A-module; then we can form the module of fractions M_f, whose elements are all fractions of the form m/f^n ($m \in M$, n an integer $\geqslant 0$). M_f is a module over the ring A_f. We may then consider the presheaf $D(f) \to M_f$, defined on the basis $\mathfrak{B} = D(f))_{f \in A}$ of X. We denote by $\widetilde{M}$ the presheaf on X which it determines. Since each M_f is an A_f-module, $\widetilde{M}$ is an $\widetilde{A}$-Module.

Proposition (9.1). $\widetilde{M}$ is a <u>sheaf</u>, and hence $\Gamma(D(f), \widetilde{M}) = M_f$ for all $f \in A$. In particular $\Gamma(X, \widetilde{M}) = M$.

<u>Proof</u>. Copy the proof of (5.1) (ii).

Since formation of modules of fractions preserves exactness, it follows that the functor $M \mapsto \widetilde{M}$ (from A-modules to

$\tilde{A}$-Modules) is exact. Moreover,

Corollary (9.2). If M, N are A-modules, then $\mathrm{Hom}_A(M, N) \cong \mathrm{Hom}_{\tilde{A}}(\tilde{M}, \tilde{N})$.

Proof. $\varphi : M \to N$ gives rise to $\varphi_f : M_f \to N_f$ for each $f \in A$, hence to $\tilde{\varphi} : \tilde{M} \to \tilde{N}$. Hence we have a homomorphism $\mathrm{Hom}_A(M, N) \to \mathrm{Hom}_{\tilde{A}}(\tilde{M}, \tilde{N})$. Conversely, given $u : \tilde{M} \to \tilde{N}$ we have $u(X) : \tilde{M}(X) \to \tilde{N}(X)$, i.e. by (9.1) a homomorphism $M \to N$. Hence a map $\mathrm{Hom}_{\tilde{A}}(\tilde{M}, \tilde{N}) \to \mathrm{Hom}_A(M, N)$. Verify that the two maps so defined are inverses of each other.

Theorem (9.3). Let $\mathfrak{F}$ be an $\tilde{A}$-Module. Then the following are equivalent:

(a) $\mathfrak{F} \cong \tilde{M}$ for some A-module M;

(b) there exists a finite open covering of X by basic open sets $D(f_i)$ such that $\mathfrak{F} \mid D(f_i) \cong \tilde{M}_i$ for some A_{f_i}-module M_i and each index i;

(c) $\mathfrak{F}$ is quasi-coherent;

(d) $\mathfrak{F}$ satisfies the following two conditions:

(d_1) for each $g \in A$ and each $s \in \mathfrak{F}(D(g))$ there exists an integer $n \geqslant 0$ such that $g^n s$ can be extended to a global section of $\mathfrak{F}$ (i.e. an element of $\mathfrak{F}(X)$);

(d_2) for each $g \in A$ and each $t \in \mathcal{F}(X)$ such that $t \mid D(g) = 0$, there exists $n \geqslant 0$ such that $g^n t = 0$.

Proof according to the scheme

$$\begin{array}{ccccc} (a) & \Rightarrow & (b) & \Leftrightarrow & (c). \\ & \Leftrightarrow\!\!\searrow & \swarrow\!\!\!\swarrow & & \\ & & (d) & & \end{array}$$

(a) ⇒ (b). Take the covering of X consisting of the single set $D(1) = X$.

(b) ⇒ (c). Since quasi-coherence is a local property, it is enough to prove (a) ⇒ (c). We have an exact sequence $A^{(I)} \to A^{(J)} \to M \to 0$, where $A^{(I)}$, $A^{(J)}$ are direct sums of copies of A; hence, since $M \mapsto \widetilde{M}$ is an exact functor, an exact functor, an exact sequence $\widetilde{A}^{(I)} \to \widetilde{A}^{(J)} \to \widetilde{M} \to 0$. Hence $\widetilde{M}$ is quasi-coherent.

(c) ⇒ (b). Each $x \in X$ has a neighbourhood $D(f)$ over which $\mathcal{F} \mid D(f)$ is the cokernel of a homomorphism $\widetilde{A}^{(I)} \mid D(f) \to \widetilde{A}^{(J)} \mid D(f)$, i.e. a homomorphism $\widetilde{A}_f^{(I)} \to \widetilde{A}_f^{(J)}$. Hence by (9.2) $\mathcal{F} \mid D(f) = \widetilde{N}$ where $N = \operatorname{coker}(A_f^{(I)} \to A_f^{(J)})$. Since X is quasi-compact, (b) is proved.

(a) ⇒ (d). If $g \in A$ and $s \in \mathcal{F}(D(g)) = M_g$, then $s = m/g^n$ for some $m \in M$ and some integer $n \geqslant 0$, hence $sg^n = m/1 =$ image of m in M_g, i.e. sg^n is the image of an element of $M = \mathcal{F}(X)$.

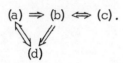

If $g \in A$, $t \in M$ and $t/1 = 0$ in M_g, then $tg^n = 0$ for some integer $n \geqslant 0$, from the basic properties of modules of fractions.

(b) $\Rightarrow$ (d). We have to show that if each $\mathfrak{F} \mid D(f_i)$ satisfies (d), then so does $\mathfrak{F}$. Take (d_2) first. We have then $g \in A$, $t \in \mathfrak{F}(X)$ and $t \mid D(g) = 0$. Then $t \mid D(gf_i) = 0$ (since $D(gf_i) = D(g) \cap D(f_i)$); hence by ($d_2$) applied to $\mathfrak{F} \mid D(f_i)$ there exists an integer $n_i \geqslant 0$ such that $(f_i g)^{n_i} t \mid D(f_i) = 0$, i.e. $(f_i g)^{n_i} t = 0$ in M_i; now f_i is a unit in A_{f_i}, hence $g^{n_i} t = 0$ in M_i. Let n be the largest of the n_i, then we have $g^n t = 0$ in each $\mathfrak{F} \mid D(f_i)$, hence $g^n t$ is the zero section of $\mathfrak{F}$.

To prove (d_1): take $g \in A$ and $s \in \mathfrak{F}(D(g))$. By applying (d_1) to $\mathfrak{F} \mid D(f_i)$, there exists an integer $n_i \geqslant 0$ and an element $s_i' \in \mathfrak{F}(D(f_i))$ which extends $(f_i g)^{n_i} s \mid D(f_i g)$. Since f_i is a unit in A_{f_i}, there exists $s_i \in \mathfrak{F}(D(f_i))$ such that $s_i' = f_i^{n_i} s_i$, and s_i extends $g^{n_i} s \mid D(f_i g)$; and we may take all the n_i to be equal, say $n_i = n$. By construction, $s_i - s_j$ restricted to $D(f_i f_j g)$ is zero; now since $\mathfrak{F} \mid D(f_i) = \widetilde{M}_i$, it follows that each $\mathfrak{F} \mid D(f_i) \cap D(f_j)$ satisfies (a) and therefore (d), hence by (d_2) applied to $\mathfrak{F} \mid D(f_i) \cap D(f_j)$ there exist integers $m_{ij} \geqslant 0$ such that $(f_i f_j g)^{m_{ij}} (s_i - s_j)$ restricted to $D(f_i) \cap D(f_j) = D(f_i f_j)$ is zero; but $f_i f_j$ is a unit in $\mathfrak{F}(D(f_i f_j))$, hence $g^m (s_i - s_j)$ restricted to

$D(f_i) \cap D(f_j)$ is zero, where $m = \max(m_{ij})$. Hence the $g^m s_i \in \Gamma(D(f_i), \mathcal{F})$ are all of them restrictions of a global section s' of $\mathcal{F}$. This section s' is an extension of $g^{m+n} s$, hence (d_1) is proved.

(d) $\Rightarrow$ (a). Let $M = \mathcal{F}(X) = \Gamma(X, \mathcal{F})$. We shall define a homomorphism $u : \widetilde{M} \to \mathcal{F}$ and show that it is an isomorphism. For this we must define $u_f : M_f \to \mathcal{F}(D(f))$ for each $f \in A$, satisfying the usual compatibility conditions. Start with the restriction homomorphism $\mathcal{F}(X) \to \mathcal{F}(D(f))$, i.e. $M \to \mathcal{F}(D(f))$. Since f is a unit in A_f, this homomorphism factorizes through M_f: $M \longrightarrow M_f \xrightarrow{u_f} \mathcal{F}(D(f))$. This defines u_f. We shall show that (d_1) implies u_f surjective, and (d_2) implies u_f injective.

Let s be any element of $\mathcal{F}(D(f))$. Then by (d_1) $f^n s$ lifts to a global section of $\mathcal{F}$, for some integer $n \geq 0$, i.e. $f^n s$ is in the image of M, hence is in $u_f(M_f)$. Hence, as f is a unit in A_f, we have $s \in u_f(M_f)$ and thus u_f is surjective.

If $z/f^n \in M_f$ is such that $u_f(z/f^n) = 0$, then $u_f(z/1) = 0$ and therefore the restriction of $z (\in \mathcal{F}(X))$ to D(f) is zero; hence by (d_2) there exists an integer $m \geq 0$ such that $zf^m = 0$; hence $z/f^n = 0$ in M_f, hence u_f is injective.

Corollary (9.4). Γ is exact on quasi-coherent Modules over an affine scheme.

Proof. Let $\mathfrak{F} \to \mathfrak{G} \to \mathfrak{H}$ be an exact sequence of quasi-coherent $\tilde{A}$-Modules. By (9.2) and (9.3) this sequence is of the form $\tilde{M} \xrightarrow{\tilde{u}} \tilde{N} \xrightarrow{\tilde{v}} \tilde{P}$ $(M = \mathfrak{F}(X)$, etc.). If $Q = \text{Im}(u)$, $R = \text{Ker}(v)$ then $\tilde{Q} = \tilde{R}$ (since the functor $M \mapsto \tilde{M}$ is exact), hence $Q = \tilde{Q}(X) = \tilde{R}(X) = R$. Hence the sequence $M \to N \to P$ is exact, i.e. the sequence $\Gamma(X, \mathfrak{F}) \to \Gamma(X, \mathfrak{G}) \to \Gamma(X, \mathfrak{H})$ is exact.

Theorem (9.5). Let A be a Noetherian ring, $\mathfrak{F}$ an $\tilde{A}$-Module. Then the following are equivalent:

(i) $\mathfrak{F}$ is coherent;

(ii) $\mathfrak{F}$ is of finite type and quasi-coherent;

(iii) $\mathfrak{F} \cong \tilde{M}$ for some finitely-generated A-module M.

Proof. (i) $\Rightarrow$ (ii) is always true (from the definitions). (ii) $\Rightarrow$ (iii): By (9.3) we have $\mathfrak{F} \cong \tilde{M}$ for some A-module M. Since $\mathfrak{F}$ is of finite type and X is quasi-compact, there exists a finite covering of X by basic open sets $D(f_i)$, and exact sequences $\tilde{A}^{p_i} \to \mathfrak{F} \to 0$ (over $D(f_i)$), i.e. exact sequences $\tilde{A}_{f_i}^{p_i} \to \tilde{M}_{f_i} \to 0$; hence, by (9.4), exact sequences $A_{f_i}^{p_i} \to M_{f_i} \to 0$. Thus each M_{f_i} is a finitely-generated A_{f_i}-module, generated say by $t_{ij}/1$ $(1 \leq j \leq p_i, t_{ij} \in M)$. Let N be the submodule of M generated by all the t_{ij}. If $z \in M$, then $z/1 \in M_{f_i}$ is of the form $\sum_j (t_{ij}/1) \cdot (a_{ij}/f_i^{m_j})$, hence $zf_i^m \in N$ for all indices i and some integer $m > 0$. Since the $D(f_i)$ cover X, the f_i^m generate the unit ideal, i.e. we have an equation of the form $\sum_i g_i f_i^m = 1$, where $g_i \in A$. Hence $z = \sum_i z f_i^m g_i \in N$, consequently $M = N$ and therefore M is finitely generated.

(iii) $\Rightarrow$ (i). Suppose $\mathfrak{F} = \widetilde{M}$ where M is a finitely generated A-module. Then we have an exact sequence of the form $A^p \to M \to 0$ for some integer $p \geq 0$, hence $\widetilde{A} \to \widetilde{M} \to 0$; thus $\widetilde{M}$ is of finite type. It remains to show that if $\widetilde{A}^p \to \widetilde{M}$ over some open set (which we may take to be D(f) for some $f \in A$), then the kernel is of finite type. We have a homomorphism $\widetilde{A}_f^p \to \widetilde{M}_f$, hence a homomorphism $A_f^p \to M_f$ by (9.2); now A_f is Noetherian (since A is), hence the kernel is finitely generated. This completes the proof.

Remark. The Noetherian assumption intervenes only in the proof of (iii) $\Rightarrow$ (i).

Corollary (9.6). If A is Noetherian, $\widetilde{A}$ is a coherent sheaf of rings.

Proposition (9.7). Let $\mathcal{F}$ be a quasi-coherent $\widetilde{A}$-Module, and let $\mathfrak{U}$ be a covering of $X = \operatorname{Spec}(A)$ by basic open sets $D(f_i)$. Then $H^p(\mathfrak{U}, \mathcal{F}) = 0$ for all $p > 0$ (and of course $H^o(\mathfrak{U}, \mathcal{F}) = \mathcal{F}(X)$).

Proof. By (9.3) we have $\mathcal{F} = \widetilde{M}$, where $M = \mathcal{F}(X)$ is an A-module. Consider the Čech resolution of $\widetilde{M}$ (Chapter 8):

$$0 \to \widetilde{M} \to \mathcal{C}^o(\mathfrak{U}, \widetilde{M}) \to \mathcal{C}^1(\mathfrak{U}, \widetilde{M}) \to \dots$$

whose sections over X form the Čech complex $0 \to M \to C^o(\mathfrak{U}, \widetilde{M}) \to C^1(\mathfrak{U}, \widetilde{M}) \to \dots$. Recall that $\mathcal{C}^q(\mathfrak{U}, \widetilde{M})$ is the sheaf associated with the presheaf

$$D(g) \mapsto \prod_\sigma \widetilde{M}(U_\sigma \cap D(g));$$

now if $\sigma = (i_o, \dots, i_q)$ we have $U_\sigma \cap D(g) = D(f_{i_o}) \cap \dots \cap D(f_{i_q}) \cap D(g) = D(f_{i_o} \dots f_{i_q} g) = D(f_\sigma g)$ say; hence $\mathcal{C}^q(\mathfrak{U}, \widetilde{M})$ is the sheaf associated with the presheaf $D(g) \mapsto \prod_\sigma M_{f_\sigma g} = (\prod_\sigma M_{f_\sigma})_g$, so that $\mathcal{C}^q(\mathfrak{U}, \widetilde{M}) = (\prod_\sigma M_{f_\sigma})^\sim$. Hence, by (9.3), the sheaf $\mathcal{C}^q(\mathfrak{U}, \widetilde{M})$ is quasi-coherent; now Γ is exact on quasi-coherent sheaves (9.4), hence the Čech complex is exact, i.e. $H^p(\mathfrak{U}, \mathcal{F}) = 0$ for all $p > 0$.

Theorem (9.8). If X is an affine scheme and $\mathcal{F}$ a quasi-coherent sheaf on X, then $H^p(X, \mathcal{F}) = 0$ for all $p > 0$.

Proof. Since finite basic open coverings are cofinal in the class of all open coverings of X, it follows from (9.7) that $\check{H}^p(X, \mathfrak{F}) = 0$ for all $p > 0$. Hence for any basic open set $U = D(f)$ we have $\check{H}^q(U, \mathfrak{F} \mid U) = 0$ for all $q > 0$ (since U is an affine open set and $\mathfrak{F} \mid U$ is quasi-coherent). Hence by Cartan's criterion (8.3) we have $\check{H}^p(X, \mathfrak{F}) = H^p(X, \mathfrak{F})$ for all $p > 0$. Hence $H^p(X, \mathfrak{F}) = 0$ for all $p > 0$.

Remark. There is another proof, due to Chevalley, of (9.8) avoiding the use of (8.3) (which we didn't prove). Let $0 \to \mathfrak{F} \to \mathcal{J}^0 \to \mathcal{J}^1 \to \dots$ be an injective resolution of a quasi-coherent sheaf $\mathfrak{F}$ on X. Then we have short exact sequences

$$(E^p): \quad 0 \to \mathcal{G}^p \to \mathcal{J}^p \to \mathcal{G}^{p+1} \to 0$$

where $\mathcal{G}^0 = \mathfrak{F}$ and $\mathcal{G}^p = \mathrm{Im}(\mathcal{J}^{p-1} \to \mathcal{J}^p)$ for $p > 0$.

Lemma (9.9). Let $f \in A$ and let $\mathfrak{U}$ be any finite covering of D(f) by basic open sets. Then $H^q(\mathfrak{U}, \mathcal{G}^p \mid D(f)) = 0$ for all $p \geq 0$ and all $q > 0$.

Proof by induction on p. True for $p = 0$ by (9.7). Let $p \geq 0$ and assume (9.9) true for this value of p (and all $q > 0$). Then $H^1(\mathfrak{U}, \mathcal{G}^p \mid D(f)) = 0$ for any finite covering of D(f) by basic open sets. Since such open coverings of D(f) are cofinal in the class of all open coverings of D(f) it follows that $\check{H}^1(D(f), \mathcal{G}^p \mid D(f)) = 0$ and therefore that $H^1(D(f), \mathcal{G}^p \mid D(f)) = 0$ (since $H^1 = \check{H}^1$ always). Hence, from the exact cohomology sequence of (E^p), we have an exact sequence

$$0 \to \mathcal{G}^p(D(f)) \to \mathcal{J}^p(D(f)) \to \mathcal{G}^{p+1}(D(f)) \to 0.$$

Since this sequence is exact for every $f \in A$, it follows that the sequence of Čech complexes

$$(*) \qquad 0 \to C^\bullet(\mathfrak{U}, \mathcal{G}^p \mid D(f)) \to C^\bullet(\mathfrak{U}, \mathcal{J}^p \mid D(f)) \to C\ (\mathfrak{U}, \mathcal{G}^{p+1} \mid D(f)) \to 0$$

is exact. Now $\mathcal{J}^p$ is injective, hence its restriction to the open set D(f) is injective and therefore the complex $C^\bullet(\mathfrak{U}, \mathcal{J}^p \mid D(f))$ is acyclic; consequently, from the cohomology exact sequence of (*), we get

$$H^q(\mathfrak{U}, \mathcal{G}^{p+1} \mid D(f)) \cong H^{q+1}(\mathfrak{U}, \mathcal{G}^p \mid D(f)) \quad (q > 0)$$

and the term on the right is zero by the inductive hypothesis.

Taking $f = 1$, $q = 1$ in (9.9), we have $H^1(\mathfrak{U}, \mathcal{G}^p) = 0$ for all $p \geqslant 0$, hence $\check{H}^1(X, \mathcal{G}^p) = 0$, hence $H^1(X, \mathcal{G}^p) = 0$. But from the exact sequences (E^p) we get (since each $\mathcal{J}^p$ is injective)

$$H^p(X, \mathfrak{F}) = H^p(X, \mathcal{G}^0) \cong H^{p-1}(X, \mathcal{G}^1) \cong \dots \cong H^1(X, \mathcal{G}^{p-1}) = 0 \quad (p > 0).$$

Theorem (9.10). If $(X, \mathcal{O}_X)$ is a scheme and $\mathfrak{F}$ is a quasi-coherent $\mathcal{O}_X$-Module, then $H^q(X, \mathfrak{F}) \cong H^q(\mathfrak{U}, \mathfrak{F})$ for any covering $\mathfrak{U}$ of X by affine open sets.

Proof. Let $\mathfrak{U} = (U_i)_{i \in I}$ be an affine open covering of X. Since X is a scheme, each $U_\sigma = U_{i_0} \cap \ldots \cap U_{i_q}$ is affine and hence by (9.8) $H^p(U_\sigma, \mathfrak{F} \mid U_\sigma) = 0$ for all σ and all $p > 0$. Hence by the comparison theorem (8.2) we have $H^p(X, \mathfrak{F}) \cong H^p(\mathfrak{U}, \mathfrak{F})$ for all $p \geq 0$.

Corollary (9.11). $H^p(X, \mathfrak{F}) \cong \check{H}^p(X, \mathfrak{F})$ under the hypotheses of (9.10).

There is a converse of (9.8):

Theorem (9.12). (Serre's criterion.) Let X be either a quasi-compact scheme or a prescheme whose underlying space is Noetherian. If $H^1(X, \mathfrak{F}) = 0$ for every quasi-coherent $\mathcal{O}_X$-Module $\mathfrak{F}$ (or even only for every quasi-coherent Ideal $\mathfrak{F}$ of $\mathcal{O}_X$), then X is an affine scheme.

For the proof we refer to (E.G.A., II, 5.2.1). (9.8) and (9.12) show that the vanishing of the $H^p(X, \mathfrak{F})$ for $p > 0$ and $\mathfrak{F}$ quasi-coherent characterizes affine schemes.

Let X be a projective algebraic variety over an algebraically closed field k, and let $\mathfrak{F}$ be a coherent $\mathcal{O}_X$-Module, where $\mathcal{O}_X$ is the sheaf of local rings on X. Serre proved that

(i) $H^q(X, \mathfrak{F}) = 0$ for $q > \dim X$;

(ii) $H^q(X, \mathfrak{F})$ is a finite-dimensional k-vector space for $0 \leqslant q \leqslant \dim X$.

The proof of (i) is easy: by (9.10) (or rather its counterpart for algebraic varieties) it is enough to find a covering of X by d + 1 affine open sets, where $d = \dim X$, and this can be achieved by intersecting X by suitably chosen hyperplanes in the projective space P in which X is embedded. (ii) is proved by reducing to the case where X = P and calculating the $H^q(P, \mathfrak{F})$ quite explicitly.

Grothendieck subsequently generalized this theorem, firstly to the case where X is complete (but not necessarily projective) and then to a statement about proper morphisms. If $f : X \to Y$ is a morphism of algebraic varieties, then f_* (Chapter 7) is a left-exact functor from $\mathcal{O}_X$-Modules to $\mathcal{O}_Y$-Modules, hence has right derived functors $R^pf_*(p \geqslant 0)$. Explicitly, if $\mathfrak{F}$ is an $\mathcal{O}_X$-Module, $R^pf_*(\mathfrak{F})$ is the sheaf on Y associated to the presheaf $U \mapsto H^p(f^{-1}(U), \mathfrak{F})$ (U open in Y). Then:

If X, Y are algebraic varieties over k, $f : X \to Y$ a <u>proper</u> morphism, $\mathfrak{F}$ a <u>coherent</u> $\mathcal{O}_X$-Module, then the 'higher direct images' $R^p f_*(\mathfrak{F})$ are coherent $\mathcal{O}_Y$-Modules. (The statement for a complete variety X is obtained by taking Y to consist of a single point.)

Finally, this theorem generalizes to the case of a proper morphism of preschemes:

Let X, Y be preschemes, Y locally Noetherian (this means that Y can be covered by affine open sets each of which is the scheme of a Noetherian ring). If $f : X \to Y$ is a proper morphism and $\mathfrak{F}$ a coherent $\mathcal{O}_X$-Module, then the $R^p f_*(\mathfrak{F})$ are coherent $\mathcal{O}_Y$-Modules (E.G.A., III, 3.2.1).

Chapter 10

THE RIEMANN-ROCH THEOREM

Throughout this chapter, X denotes a nonsingular, irreducible, projective algebraic variety defined over an algebraically closed field k (of any characteristic). A <u>divisor</u> D on X is an element of the free abelian group generated by the irreducible closed subvarieties of codimension 1 in X: $D = \Sigma n_i D_i$, where the n_i are integers and the D_i are irreducible subvarieties of codimension 1. D is <u>positive</u> (notation $D \geqslant 0$) if each $n_i \geqslant 0$.

Since X is irreducible it has a field of rational functions, k(X). Any non-zero $f \in k(X)$ defines a divisor (f) = (zeros of f) - (poles of f). Two divisors D_1, D_2 are <u>linearly equivalent</u> (notation $D_1 \equiv D_2$) if $D_1 - D_2$ is the divisor of some rational function. Clearly this is an equivalence relation. The set of all positive divisors linearly equivalent to a divisor D is denoted by $|D|$. A closely related object is the k-vector space L(D), which consists of 0 and all $f \in k(X)$ such that

$D + (f) \geq 0$. Thus the $f \in L(D)$ give rise to the divisors in $|D|$, and $|D|$ may be regarded as the projective space associated to the vector space $L(D)$.

We shall see in a moment that $L(D)$ is finite-dimensional. Its dimension is denoted by $\ell(D)$, and $\dim|D| = \ell(D) - 1$. It is largely a matter of taste whether we work with $|D|$ or $L(D)$.

The Riemann-Roch theorem, in its original conception, is concerned with evaluating $\ell(D)$ (or $\dim|D|$) in terms of other characters of D and X. One such character of X is the <u>arithmetic genus</u> $p_a(X)$, defined by

$$1 + (-1)^n p_a(X) = \chi(X) = \sum_{i=0}^{d} (-1)^i \dim_k H^i(X, \mathcal{O}_X),$$

where $d = \dim X$.

There is a distinguished equivalence class of divisors on X, called the <u>canonical</u> divisor class (definition later). A canonical divisor is denoted by K.

THE RIEMANN-ROCH THEOREM FOR A CURVE

If X is a curve, a divisor D on X is of the form $\Sigma n_i P_i$, where P_i are points of X. Hence we may define the <u>degree</u> of D: $\deg D = \Sigma n_i$. If D is the divisor of a rational function, then $\deg D = 0$ (number of zeros = number of poles); hence deg D depends only on the equivalence class of D. Riemann proved (for the case where k is the field of complex numbers) that

$$\dim |D| \geqslant \deg D - g$$

where $g = p_a(X) = \dim_k H^1(X, \mathcal{O}_X)$ is the genus of X; and Roch a few years later made this inequality more precise:

$$\dim |D| = \deg D - g + i(D) \qquad (1)$$

where i(D), the index of speciality of D, is defined to be $\ell(K - D)$, that is to say the number of linearly independent divisors $D \leqslant K$, where K is a fixed canonical divisor. Thus (1) may be rewritten in the form

$$\ell(D) - \ell(K - D) = \deg D + \chi(X) \qquad (1')$$

where $\chi(X) = 1 - g$. In particular (D = 0) $\ell(K) = g$, hence (D = K) $\deg K = 2g - 2$.

THE RIEMANN-ROCH THEOREM FOR A SURFACE

If X is a surface and C, D are divisors on X their intersection number C.D is defined; C.D is a symmetric bilinear function of C and D, and is zero if either C or D is linearly equivalent to 0. The degree of a divisor D is deg D = D.D; again this depends only on the equivalence class of D. A divisor D has another numerical invariant, its virtual genus $\pi(D)$, which is defined as follows. Suppose first that C is an irreducible non-singular curve on X, and K any canonical divisor. Then K + C cuts out a canonical divisor on the curve C, hence the genus g of C is given by $2g - 2 = C.(K + C)$. We use this formula to define the virtual genus of a divisor D, namely

$$2\pi(D) - 2 = D.(K + D).$$

Then the Riemann-Roch theorem for a surface (Castelnuovo, 1896) is

$$\dim|D| \geqslant \deg D + 1 - \pi(D) + p_a(X) - i(D) \tag{2}$$

where as before i(D) is the 'index of speciality' of D, i.e. $i(D) = \ell(K - D)$. Thus (2) may be rewritten in the form

$$\ell(D) + \ell(K - D) > D.D - \frac{1}{2}D.\ (K + D) + \chi(X)$$
$$= \frac{1}{2}D.\ (D - K) + \chi(X). \tag{2'}$$

In contrast to (1'), this is still an inequality. The difference between the two sides is called the superabundance s(D): thus

$$\ell(D) - s(D) + \ell(K - D) = \frac{1}{2}D.\ (D - K) + \chi(X) \tag{2''}$$

where s(D) is some non-negative integer.

The next stage is to reinterpret (1') and (2") in cohomological terms.

THE LINE-BUNDLE ASSOCIATED WITH A DIVISOR

Let X be of arbitrary dimension, $D = \Sigma n_i D_i$ a divisor on X, and let (U_α) be a covering of X by affine open sets. In the affine variety U_α each hypersurface D_i is given by a single equation $f_{i\alpha} = 0$, where $f_{i\alpha}$ belongs to the coordinate ring $A(U_\alpha)$ of U_α, hence we may associate with D the rational function $g_\alpha = \prod_i f_{i\alpha}^{n_i}$; g_α belongs to the field of fractions of $A(U_\alpha)$ [since X is irreducible, so is U_α, hence $A(U_\alpha)$ is an integral domain], and this field of fractions is just k(X). The divisor cut out by D on the open set U_α is the divisor of the rational function g_α. Thus for each α we have $g_\alpha \in k(X)$, such that $h_{\alpha\beta} = g_\alpha g_\beta^{-1}$ is finite and non-zero at every point of $U_\alpha \cap U_\beta$: hence $h_{\alpha\beta}$ defines a regular map $U_\alpha \cap U_\beta \to k^*$ (the multiplicative group of k), such that $h_{\alpha\alpha} = 1$, $h_{\alpha\beta} h_{\beta\gamma} = h_{\alpha\gamma}$ in $U_\alpha \cap U_\beta \cap U_\gamma$. Hence the functions $h_{\alpha\beta}$ define a line-bundle {D}, and it is not difficult to see that (i) {D} depends (up to isomorphism) only on D, and not on the covering (U_α); (ii) equivalent divisors give rise to isomorphic line-bundles.

Conversely, a line bundle on X gives rise to a class of divisors, and L(D) is isomorphic to the vector space of global cross-sections of the bundle $\{D\}$.

Equivalently, we may consider the sheaf $\mathcal{L}(D)$ of germs of cross-sections of the bundle $\{D\}$. $\mathcal{L}(D)$ is an $\mathcal{O}_X$-Module, locally isomorphic to $\mathcal{O}_X$ and therefore coherent. If U is an open set in X, then $\Gamma(U, \mathcal{L}(D))$ is the set of all $f \in k(X)$ such that $(f) + D \geq 0$ on U, so that in particular $(U = X)$ L(D) is the space of global sections of $\mathcal{L}(D)$:

$$L(D) = H^0(X, \mathcal{L}(D)).$$

Since $\mathcal{L}(D)$ is coherent, L(D) is finite-dimensional by Serre's theorem quoted at the end of Chapter 9.

Next, let T be the (covariant) tangent bundle of X, whose fibre T_x at a point $x \in X$ is the space of all tangent vectors to X at x (this may be defined algebraically as the dual of the k-vector space $\underline{m}_x/\underline{m}_x^2$, where $\underline{m}_x$ is the maximal ideal of the local ring of X at x). The fibre T_x is of dimension n, hence the nth exterior power $\Lambda^n T$ is a line-bundle. The corresponding divisor class is the canonical class on X.

SERRE'S DUALITY THEOREM

Let D be a divisor on X, K a canonical divisor. Let

$$h^i(D) = \dim_k H^i(X, \mathcal{L}(D))$$

(finite since $\mathcal{L}(D)$ is coherent). The duality theorem states (or rather implies) that

$$h^i(D) = h^{d-i}(K - D), \quad 0 \leqslant i \leqslant d \quad (d = \dim X).$$

Since $\ell(D) = \dim L(D) = \dim H^0(X, \mathcal{L}(D)) = h^0(D)$, the Riemann-Roch theorem (1') for a curve now takes the form

$$h^0(D) - h^1(D) = \deg D + \chi(X)$$

or

$$\chi(D) = \deg D + \chi(X) \tag{1''}$$

where in general

$$\chi(D) = \sum_{i \geqslant 0} (-1)^i h^i(D);$$

and for a surface it turns out that the superabundance $s(D)$ is just $h^1(D)$, so that the Riemann-Roch theorem (2'') for a surface takes the form

$$\chi(D) = \frac{1}{2}D. \ (D - K) + \chi(X). \tag{2'''}$$

THE CHOW RING

Let X be as before (nonsingular, irreducible, projective). A <u>cycle</u> on X is a formal linear combination of irreducible subvarieties of X. Thus a divisor is a cycle of codimension 1. Two cycles D_0, D_1 on X are rationally equivalent if there exists a cycle C on the product variety $X \times k$ such that C intersects $X \times \{0\}$ and $X \times \{1\}$ properly (i.e. so that all components of the intersection have the right dimensions) in the cycles $D_0 \times \{0\}$ and $D_1 \times \{1\}$ respectively. For divisors, rational equivalence is the same as linear equivalence.

If C, D are cycles, their intersection C . D is defined only if C, D intersect properly. If C, D do not intersect properly, it can be shown that D can be replaced by an equivalent cycle D' such that C . D' is defined, and the rational equivalence class of C . D' is independent of the choice of the cycle D'. Hence we have a product defined on the group A(X) of classes of cycles with respect to rational equivalence. A(X) is a graded group: $A(X) = \bigoplus_{i=0}^{d} A^i(X)$, where d = dim X and $A^i(X)$ consists of the classes of cycles of codimension i in X. The multiplication just defined on A(X) respects this grading, so that A(X) is a graded ring, called the Chow ring of X. It is commutative and associative and has an identity element. A(X) serves for some purposes as a replacement for the cohomology ring $H^*(X, \underline{Z})$ which is defined when k is the field of complex numbers; but in general it is much bigger (consider e.g. a curve of genus > 0).

$A(X)$ has good functorial properties, corresponding to those of the cohomology ring of a manifold. First, if $f : X \to Y$ is a regular map (or morphism of algebraic varieties) then f^{-1}(cycle) is a cycle on X, and this operation is compatible with intersections and rational equivalence, hence defines a graded ring homomorphism

$$f^* : A(Y) \to A(X).$$

Next, if $f : X \to Y$ is proper, then the image of a Zariski-closed set in X is closed in Y, which enables us to define

$$f_* : A(X) \to A(Y).$$

f_* is an additive homomorphism, but not multiplicative, and does not respect the grading. However, there is the so-called projection formula

$$f_*(x . f^*(y)) = f_*(x) . y \quad (x \in A(X),\ y \in A(Y)).$$

CHERN CLASSES OF A VECTOR BUNDLE

Let E be a vector bundle on X, say of rank q (this means $\dim E_x = q$ for each $x \in X$). We shall associate with E elements $c_i(E) \in A^i(X) \quad (0 \leqslant i \leqslant q)$, where in particular $c_0(E) = 1$, called the <u>Chern classes</u> of X. There are various ways of defining these classes constructively, and they can also be characterized uniquely by the following axioms:

(i) <u>Functoriality</u>. Given $f : Y \to X$, then $c_i(f^*(E)) = f^*c_i(E)$ $(i \geq 0)$, where $f^*(E)$ is the inverse image bundle on Y;

(ii) <u>Normalization</u>. If E is a line bundle, say $E = \{D\}$, then $c_1(E)$ is the class of D in $A^1(X)$.

(iii) <u>Additivity</u>. If $0 \to E' \to E \to E'' \to 0$ is an exact sequence of vector bundles on X, then

$$c_i(D) = \sum_{j+k=i} c_j(E')c_k(E'').$$

If we define the <u>total Chern class</u> of E to be the sum $c(E) = \sum_{i \geq 0} c_i(E)$, then (iii) takes the form

$$c(E) = c(E')c(E'').$$

The following formalism, due to Hirzebruch, is very convenient. Let t be an indeterminate, and factorize $1 + c_1(E)t + c_2(E)t^2 + \ldots + c_q(E)t^q$ formally: say

$$1 + c_1t + \ldots + c_qt^q = \prod_{i=1}^{q} (1 + \gamma_i t),$$

and call the γ_i the 'Chern roots' of E. Then it can be shown that, if E' is another vector bundle on X with Chern roots γ_j', then the Chern roots of $E \otimes E'$ are $\gamma_i + \gamma_j'$; the Chern roots of the dual E^* of E are $-\gamma_i$; and the Chern roots of the exterior power $\Lambda^p E$ are $\gamma_{i_1} + \gamma_{i_2} + \ldots + \gamma_{i_p}$ $(i_1 < \ldots < i_p)$. The Chern character of E is defined to be

$$ch(E) = e^{\gamma_1} + e^{\gamma_2} + \ldots + e^{\gamma_q} (q = \text{rank } E) \in A(X) \otimes \mathbb{Q}$$

where e^γ means the exponential series $1 + \gamma + \frac{1}{2}\gamma^2 + \ldots$, which here is effectively a finite sum since A(X) is zero in dimensions $> d = \dim X$. From axiom (iii) it follows that if $0 \to E' \to E \to E'' \to 0$ is an exact sequence of vector bundles on X, then

$$ch(E') - ch(E) + ch(E'') = 0$$

i.e. the function ch is additive. It is also multiplicative: $ch(E \otimes F) = ch(E) . ch(F)$.

We have another additive function at hand: if E is a vector bundle, let $\mathcal{E}$ denote its sheaf of germs of local sections; then $\mathcal{E}$ is a coherent sheaf and therefore the expression

$$\chi(X, E) = \sum_{i \geq 0} (-1)^i \dim_k H^i(X, \mathcal{E})$$

is a well-defined integer. If $0 \to E' \to E \to E'' \to 0$ is an exact sequence of bundles, then the sequence of sheaves $0 \to \mathcal{E}' \to \mathcal{E} \to \mathcal{E}'' \to 0$ is exact, and from the cohomology sequence of this we deduce that

$$\chi(X, E') - \chi(X, E) + \chi(X, E'') = 0$$

by counting up the dimensions.

HIRZEBRUCH'S RIEMANN-ROCH THEOREM

Let T^* be the contravariant tangent bundle of X, i.e. the dual of T. Its Chern classes $c_i(T^*)$ are called the Chern classes of X: notation $c_i(X)$. If γ_i are the Chern roots of T^*, then $-\gamma_i$ are the Chern roots of T, hence $c_1(\Lambda^n T) = -\Sigma\gamma_i = -c_1(X)$. By the second axiom for Chern classes $-c_1(X)$ is the class of a canonical divisor K.

The Todd class of X, $\tau(X)$, is defined to be

$$\tau(X) = \prod_{i=1}^{d} \gamma_i/(1 - e^{-\gamma_i}) \quad (d = \dim X)$$

with the usual understanding that the product on the right is to be expanded out as a power series in the γ_i; since it is a symmetric function of the γ_i it can be written as a power series in the Chern classes $c_i(X)$, hence is an element of $A(X) \otimes \mathbb{Q}$ ($\mathbb{Q}$ = field of rational numbers). Then Hirzebruch's theorem is the formula

$$\chi(D) = \varkappa_d[\mathrm{ch}(\{D\})\tau(X)] \tag{3}$$

where D is any divisor on X, $\{D\}$ the associated line bundle, $\chi(D)$ the alternating sum $\sum_{i\geq 0}(-1)^i h^i(D)$ $= \sum_{i\geq 0}(-1)^i \dim_k H^i(X, \mathfrak{L}(D))$; and the symbol $\varkappa_d[\,]$ means that we take the homogeneous component of degree d of the expression inside the brackets, which is an element of $A^d(X) \otimes \underline{Q} \cong \underline{Z} \otimes \underline{Q} \cong \underline{Q}$. (Thus the right hand side of (3) is *a priori* only a rational number.)

Let us show for example how to recover from (3) the Riemann-Roch theorem for an algebraic surface, in the form (2'''). First take D = 0 in (3), then $\chi(D) = \chi(X) (= 1 + p_a(X))$, hence

$$\begin{aligned}\chi(X) &= \varkappa_2\left[\frac{\gamma_1}{1 - e^{-\gamma_1}} \cdot \frac{\gamma_2}{1 - e^{-\gamma_2}}\right] \\ &= \varkappa_2\left[\left(1 - \frac{1}{2}\gamma_1 + \frac{1}{6}\gamma_1^2\right)^{-1} \cdot \left(1 - \frac{1}{2}\gamma_2 + \frac{1}{6}\gamma_2^2\right)^{-1}\right] \\ &= \varkappa_2\left[\left(1 + \frac{1}{2}\gamma_1 + \frac{1}{12}\gamma_1^2\right)\left(1 + \frac{1}{2}\gamma_2 + \frac{1}{12}\gamma_2^2\right)\right] \\ &= \frac{1}{12}(\gamma_1^2 + \gamma_2^2) + \frac{1}{4}\gamma_1\gamma_2 = \frac{1}{12}(c_1^2 + c_2) \quad (c_i = c_i(X)).\end{aligned}$$

Hence, if $d = c_1(\{D\})$ is the class of D in $A^1(X)$, we have

$$\begin{aligned}\chi(D) &= \varkappa_2[e^d \tau(X)] \\ &= \varkappa_2\left[\left(1 + d + \frac{1}{2}d^2\right)\left(1 + \frac{1}{2}c_1 + \frac{1}{12}(c_1^2 + c_2)\right)\right] \\ &= \frac{1}{12}(c_1^2 + c_2) + \frac{1}{2}d^2 + \frac{1}{2}dc_1 \\ &= \frac{1}{2}d \cdot (d + c_1) + \chi(X) = \frac{1}{2}D \cdot (D - K) + \chi(X)\end{aligned}$$

since c_1 is the class of -K.

Remark. The theorem actually proved by Hirzebruch was the formula (3) for a divisor D on a <u>complex</u> projective variety, the Chern classes being elements of the cohomology ring $H^*(X, \underline{Z})$.

The formula (3) generalizes to any vector bundle E on X (not necessarily a line bundle):

$$\chi(X, E) = \varkappa_d [ch(E) \,.\, \tau(X)]. \tag{3'}$$

This is the most general form of Hirzebruch's Riemann-Roch theorem.

THE GROTHENDIECK GROUP K(X)

Let X be as before and let F(X) be the free abelian group generated by the (isomorphism classes of) coherent $\mathcal{O}_X$-Modules: so that an element of F(X) is a formal linear combination $x = \Sigma n_i \mathfrak{F}_i$ of coherent $\mathcal{O}_X$-Modules. Corresponding to each short exact sequence (E) : $0 \to \mathfrak{F}' \to \mathfrak{F} \to \mathfrak{F}'' \to 0$, let Q(E) denote the element $\mathfrak{F}' - \mathfrak{F} + \mathfrak{F}'' \in F(X)$, and let $K_*(X)$ denote the quotient of F(X) by the subgroup generated by all elements Q(E), as E runs through all exact sequences.

The group $K_*(X)$ has an obvious universal property. A function φ, defined on the class of coherent $\mathcal{O}_X$-Modules, with values in an abelian group G is said to be additive if $\varphi(\mathfrak{F}') - \varphi(\mathfrak{F}) + \varphi(\mathfrak{F}'') = 0$ whenever $0 \to \mathfrak{F}' \to \mathfrak{F} \to \mathfrak{F}'' \to 0$ is exact. Then every additive function φ factors through $K_*(X)$, i.e. induces a homomorphism $K_*(X) \to G$.

We may perform the same construction with vector bundles on X in place of coherent sheaves. This gives us another group $K^*(X)$. Each vector bundle E has a sheaf of local sections, which is locally free (i.e., locally isomorphic to $\mathfrak{O}_X^n$ for some n) and therefore coherent. Equivalently, we can define $K^*(X)$ in terms of locally free sheaves.

If E is a vector bundle on X, tensoring with E is an exact operation and therefore gives rise to a product in $K^*(X)$. This product is clearly associative and commutative, and the class of the trivial line bundle is the identity element. Hence we have a commutative ring structure on $K^*(X)$.

If $\mathcal{E}$ is a locally free sheaf on X, tensoring with $\mathcal{E}$ is an exact operation and therefore gives rise to a product $K^*(X) \times K_*(X) \to K_*(X)$, which makes $K_*(X)$ into a $K^*(X)$-module.

Let $f : X \to Y$ be a regular map. If E is a vector bundle on Y, then its inverse image $f^*(E)$ is a bundle on X. The functor f^* is exact and therefore defines $f^! : K^*(Y) \to K^*(X)$, which is a ring homomorphism since f^* is compatible with tensor product of bundles.

Next, let $f : X \to Y$ be a proper map. We cannot define the direct image of a bundle but we can define the direct image of a sheaf. If $\mathfrak{F}$ is a coherent $\mathcal{O}_X$-Module, then by the finiteness theorem quoted at the end of Chapter 9 the higher direct images $R^q f_*(\mathfrak{F})$ $(q \geq 0)$ are coherent $\mathcal{O}_Y$-Modules which vanish for $q > \dim X$. Define

$$f_!(\mathfrak{F}) = \sum_{q \geq 0} (-1)^q R^q f_*(\mathfrak{F}).$$

The right-hand side of this formula is additive in $\mathfrak{F}$ (from the exact sequence of derived functors, (8.1)) and hence induces a homomorphism of abelian groups

$$f_! : K_*(X) \to K_*(Y).$$

As in the case of the Chow ring, there is a "projection formula"

$$f_!(f^!(y)x) = yf_!(x) \quad (y \in K^*(Y),\ x \in K_*(X))$$

which says that, if we regard $K_*(X)$ as a $K^*(Y)$-module via $f^!$, then $f_!$ is a $K^*(Y)$-module homomorphism.

Since $K^*(X)$ can be defined in terms of locally free coherent sheaves, it follows that we have an (additive) homomorphism $\mathcal{E} : K^*(X) \to K_*(X)$. It can be shown that, if X is irreducible, nonsingular and quasi-projective (which means isomorphic to an open subset of a projective variety) then $\mathcal{E}$ is an isomorphism.

Remark. $K^*(X)$ has most of the formal properties of a cohomology ring, except for the dimension axiom (it is not a graded ring). Similarly $K_*(X)$ has the formal properties of homology, apart from dimension. The theorem $K_* \cong K^*$ when X is nonsingular and quasi-projective should be regarded as a statement of Poincaré duality. From now on we shall identify K_* and K^* by means of $\mathcal{E}$, and denote them both by K.

We remarked earlier than the Chern character ch is additive: if $0 \to E' \to E \to E'' \to 0$ is an exact sequence of vector bundles on X, then $ch(E') - ch(E) + ch(E'') = 0$: hence we have

$$ch : K(X) \to A(X) \otimes Q$$

which is a ring homomorphism. How does this behave with respect to the homomorphisms $f^!$ and $f_!$? Take $f^!$ first: let $f : X \to Y$ be a regular map. From the functoriality of Chern classes we have $ch(f^*(E)) = f^*(ch(E))$ and therefore the diagram

$$\begin{array}{ccc} K(X) & \xrightarrow{ch} & A(X) \otimes \underline{Q} \\ {\scriptstyle f^!}\uparrow & & \uparrow \\ K(Y) & \xrightarrow[ch]{} & A(Y) \otimes \underline{Q} \end{array}$$

GROTHENDIECK'S RIEMANN-ROCH THEOREM

The answer to the same question for $f_!$ (where the map $f: X \to Y$ is now proper) is the Riemann-Roch theorem of Grothendieck: the diagram

$$\begin{array}{ccc} K(X) & \xrightarrow{\tau(X)ch} & A(X) \otimes \underline{Q} \\ {\scriptstyle f_!}\downarrow & & \uparrow \\ K(Y) & \xrightarrow[\tau(Y)ch]{} & A(Y) \otimes \underline{Q} \end{array}$$

is commutative, i.e.

$$f_*(\tau(X)ch(x)) = \tau(Y)ch(f_!(x)) \text{ for any } x \in A(X). \tag{4}$$

This includes Hirzebruch's Riemann-Roch theorem (3') as the special case in which Y is taken to be a single point. A coherent sheaf on Y is then a finite-dimensional vector space, hence the dimension function gives an isomorphism $K(Y) \cong \underline{Z}$. If $\mathfrak{F}$ is a coherent sheaf on X, then $f_!(\mathfrak{F}) = \Sigma(-1)^q R^q f_*(\mathfrak{F})$ $= \Sigma(-1)^q H^q(X, \mathfrak{F})$ (since f_* is now the section functor Γ). We have $A^o(Y) = \underline{Z}$, $A^i(Y) = 0$ for $i > 0$, hence $f_*(\tau(X)ch(\mathfrak{F}))$ $= \varkappa_d[ch(\mathfrak{F})\tau(X)]$; finally $\tau(Y) = 1$ and hence (4) reduces to

$$\chi(X, \mathfrak{F}) = \varkappa_d[\mathrm{ch}(\mathfrak{F})\tau(X)] \tag{3''}$$

which is Hirzebruch's Riemann-Roch theorem stated for a coherent sheaf rather than a vector bundle E. However this generality over (3') is illusory, since both sides of (3") are additive in the argument $\mathfrak{F}$.

Grothendieck's proof consists in factorizing the morphism f into an injection $g : X \to P \times Y$ (where P is a projective space containing X and $g(x) = (x, f(x))$) followed by a projection $h : P \times Y \to Y$. It is enough to prove (4) for each of g and h separately; the proof for h can be reduced to the case where Y is a point, i.e. to the Hirzebruch theorem (3') for a projective space P; the proof for g is more difficult and is achieved by first taking the case where the subvariety g(X) of $P \times Y$ is of codimension 1, and then reducing the general case to this by blowing up the subvariety g(X).

BIBLIOGRAPHY

Since there are hardly any references to the literature in the text, the following indications (which are of course incomplete) may be of use.

For sheaf theory and homological algebra:

R. Godement, Théorie des Faisceaux, Hermann, Paris, 1958;

A. Grothendieck, Sur quelques points d'algèbre Homologique, Tokoku Math. J., **9**, 119-221 (1957).

For cohomological methods in algebraic geometry:

F. Hirzebruch, Topological Methods in Algebraic Geometry, 3rd edition, Springer, Berlin, 1966;

J.-P. Serre, Faisceaux algèbriques cohérents, Ann. Math., **61**, 197-278 (1955).

The theory of schemes is expounded in

A. Grothendieck and J. Dieudonné, Éléments de Géometrie Algèbrique, 0, I, II, III, IV, ..., Publ. Math. de l'Institut des Hautes Études Scientifiques, nos. 4, 7, 11, 17, 20, 24, 28, 32, ...

For the Hirzebruch-Riemann-Roch theorem, see

Hirzebruch's book cited above; for Grothendieck's version, see

A. Borel and J.-P. Serre: Le théorème de Riemann-Roch (d'après Grothendieck), Bull. Soc. Math. France, **86**, 97-136 (1958),

and the references given there.